DA VAAM O' DA SKYNBOW

Stories of Shetland Music

By Tom Morton

In memory of Bobby Campbell

Published by Shetland Library,
Lower Hillhead, Lerwick, Shetland ZE1 0EL

ISBN: 0 904562 84 0

Printed by Shetland Litho, Lerwick.

CONTENTS

ILLUSTRATIONS

INTRODUCTION
Northernmost

1978, and the Viscount runs into what feels like a brick wall, high over the Highlands. The old aeroplane, its picture-window portholes shivering, literally stops dead in the air, then drops like a failed lift. Judders to a halt again, begins to pitch. Everyone is too stunned for fear. Then the panic kicks in, half calmed by the pilot's intercom squawk: we will not be flying on to Shetland. We will, instead, be landing at Inverness.

An hour's wait in a toy terminal. Another hour. Free sandwiches - a novelty in those days. Then news: those who still want to go to Shetland can go by bus to Aberdeen, where bookings have been made for them aboard the ferry *St Clair*. Fine, I think. Still make it by tonight.

I am a young journalist doing an oil story, the oil story of the moment, and I have an idea that Shetland floats just above Wick. Or that Orkney and Shetland are the same. Actually, I have no idea at all. When we arive at the gale-lashed dockside, a huge pale blue and white ship towers over me. A right-enough, ocean-going sort of affair, it seems to me. Good grief, I think. How long is the crossing, I ask someone,

thinking Arran, thinking Millport. Fourteen hours, they reply. And I am sure this is a mistake, or a joke.

"Mind you" they say "she's only running on one engine at the moment."

Aha! so how long does she take running on both engines?

"Fourteen hours."

I hear no music, see little that is picturesque. It is the miry pit of winter, and I am running around in a hired Mini, back and forth from Lerwick to the crazed multimillion shambles which is The Site: Sullom Voe. Everything is dark, or brutally floodlit. Hardline shadows, scoured with hail, rain, sleet and snow. There is construction sand, concrete and mud, it seems, on every surface in Shetland indoors and out. One day I drive right onto the single completed loading jetty, unbothered, unaccosted. An Edinburgh man in a quarry hut tells me with wonder in his voice that last night, he helped kill a sheep, and drank a colossal quantity of rum. The two go together, he says. I simply cannot imagine such a thing. The entire place seems so....elemental. I buy some Fair Isle gloves and go home to Glasgow. By the time I give the Mini back, nothing on it works. I mean *nothing*. I have to push it into its parking spot at Sumburgh, where Portacabins appear to be breeding in a sea of yellow mud.

The opening of the OIL base, and Ocean Inchcape fly me to Sumburgh from Dundee, of all places. Cold and blustery, but bright. An excellent meal at the Lerwick Hotel. A small, bespectacled woman with a Uher tape recorder trying to shield a microphone from the wind on the flat, wide concrete pier. "Have you been here before?" Yes. No music.

Seven years later, and I am in the Lounge, that friendly aroma of cigarette smoke, beer, old carpet, perfume and sweat catching at my throat. And there is music, loads of it. Later, I am prevented from entering Posers, ostensibly because I am wearing a leather jacket. This when I am on the guest list for every major nightclub in Scotland. I am dumbfounded. Inside, I can see two men propping up the bar, dressed in blue boiler suits and white wellington boots. "Take it off or leave" says someone whose muscles have muscles. I take it off.

Within a month, I am back, with a television crew, filming some segments for a religious magazine programme called Voyager. For whatever reason, we need live music, and the woman for whose sake I have organised the entire trip introduces me to Kenny Johnson, Brian Nicholson, Lynne Nicholson, Roy Tait, Norma Farmer. The first of many manifestations of Scrape the Barrel I am to encounter. We talk guitars. I have a Gibson, Brian has a Martin. A Martin!

4

This far north? Extraordinary!

Six months later, I have moved north to the Land of Martins; me, an ancient and dangerous Ford Cortina Estate, 200 records, a Gibson J40, a load of books and some clothes. Susan has told me I need only earn enough for "Marlboro and whisky". I contemplate a job at what is still The Site. Somehow, I end up news editor of *The Shetland Times*, working for a large bearded person called Jonathan Wills. He is some kind of doctor, and has an inflatable boat.

Music takes over my life. CADE, the Campaign Against Dounreay Expansion, seems to be having benefit gigs every third day. I play at one, nervous, singing some of the songs salvaged from half-baked attempts at the Glasgow rock scene. Dave Hammond, of all people, plays the fiddle, and very well too. Brian Nicholson and I form a duo, then a band, modestly called the Zetland Beat and Rhythm Kings. I play with the moveable feast which is Scrape the Barrel on and off, too. At two folk festivals. There seems to be music coming up through the peat. The Arts Trust gives us some cash, and a wee record label is formed: Hjaltland Phono-graphic Industries. Shetland Calling, a compilation tape, is released, featuring Mary White, Scrape the Barrel, Debbie Scott and John o' da Burns, Morton and Nicholson. It sells out. Brian and I record a further tape at the Old Haa in

Burravoe, Stormbound. It is savaged by Folk Roots but enjoyed by the New Shetlander. Not a lot of people buy it. There are other bands, other musicians: Alex Johnson and Ian Barrie, both of whom, I do not find out until a decade later, once played in the seminal Shetland rock group Rainbow Pavement. Neil Scollay from Yell, Big Davie Nicholson, Hamish Henderson, Ian Leask, Kipper Anderson. And guitars by the truckload.

Kenny Johnson has his shop, the Shetland Luthiers. I hang out there. I end up with two Martins, but before that there is a black Gibson 335. The wee nyaff from Texas - not Sharleen - nearly buys it off me. Instead, Neil Scollay does. A Tokai Telecaster is acquired. A G&L, the last guitar made by Leo Fender; and briefly a Strat and a Gurian. Instruments become a kind of sickness.

And the lore, the yarns: tales of Peerie Willie, sledging down one of the lanes during a snowstorm. On a double bass. The Man Who Always Had Breakfast In America, and had more adventures than Vasco De Gama on that legendary tour before the rest of the Boys of the Lough got out of bed. Much more. Playing pool with the man himself in the Thule, and being soundly thrashed. The bands and the characters: Hom Bru, Pete Stack, the first and second Shetland rock festivals. No Sweat, the River Detectives insisting on doing no more than 20 minutes per set, and being thrown out of the Voe Tavern. Eliot Davis, manager of Wet Wet Wet, at the Booth in Hillswick. An amazing gig with Country Harmony at the Scalloway Legion. Riots at the Fisherman's Arms, a great night at the Crofter's in Ollaberry. Being banned from Whalsay. Elvis Costello and Nick Lowe duetting at the Garrison. Visiting punks Toxik Efex phoning in high dudgeon when I insist on Radio Shetland that they would benefit from the application of a baseball bat. Open air all-day drinking and playing at the Booth in Hillswick. The amazing sight of We Free Kings at the TA Hall during Up Helly Aa, almost catatonic on magic mushrooms. Arguments, dissension, fallings out and makings-up. Gradually realising that the days of dreaming were ending, that life as professional musician did not beckon after all, despite all the gifts and pleasure Shetland had provided.

Forming the stripped-down band Rockhopper Trawl; gigs at the Ferry Inn where three people came to hear us, John Robertson always faithfully among them. Gradually growing dispirited at the need to play I'm A Believer every night, three times. Going on Radio Shetland and saying I would never play in Shetland again, because no-one was interested in original material. An extraordinary "Rent Party" at Islesburgh which ended in a near riot, outrage from the

Islesburgh Committee and a lot of vomiting. Leaving for four years. Coming back.

And now this.

Richard Wemyss' paintings and the accompanying CD together reflect the new confidence and growth in Shetland music. The talent has always been here, but as Stephen King says, talent is a blunt knife which has to be delivered with enormous force. Shetland is nowadays a name to conjure with across the continents, a name which sells. Which, under the guidance of Davie Gardner, will become even more a badge of excellence. Singer-songwriters are refusing to hide, original material is no longer so much of a local handicap. Bands are experimenting with old and new influences. The accessibility of recording and duplicating technology has made releasing a CD an option for anyone with a decent run of gigs to sell them at. And the heritage left, still being left, by the great names - Tammy Anderson, Aly Bain, Ronnie Cooper, Willie Johnson, Willie Hunter, Billy Kay, Violet Tulloch, Trevor Hunter - is being nurtured by the fantastic teaching programme in schools throughout the isles. The fruits are being reaped. It would be a mistake, too, to underestimate the contribution of the late Malcolm Green, in engineering the folk festival and turning it into an international phenomenon.

At first, I thought I was going to write some sort of definitive history, The Story Of Shetland Music. Then I realised that space, time and my own limitations would allow nothing remotely like that. I was concerned too at delving into still-raw controversies, at causing offence by failing to mention names, places or events crucial to some interpretations of the music's growth. And then I thought of simply telling some tales: Stories of Shetland Music.

Here they are. The truth, you might say, is in here, but told often by fictional characters; telescoped, stretched. The words of very real people are here too, though, and as carefully as I could I have checked their accuracy.

I have to thank various people and organisations for their help in researching what has become Da Vaam o' da Skynbow: if I have inadvertently excluded anyone, forgive me:

Alistair Clark, author of the Aly Bain biography *Fiddler On The Loose* which he has generously allowed me to ransack for my own nefarious purposes, who spent a morning with me in the shadow of the Forth Rail Bridge. Davie Gardner and John Robertson. The Shetland Archives and all who sail in her. Mary Blance, who has I hope saved me from lynching over my attempts at reproducing Shetland dialect and grammar. Vaila Wishart, and *The Shetland Times*, for emergency printing and gratefully-received work. Drew Ratter, who agrees with me reasonably often about music. Brian Nicholson co-wrote the song *This Guitar Says Goodbye*, coming up with the plot, which I have adapted into the story included here. Robbie Shepherd, whose interview with Tom Anderson, as reproduced in the *Shetland Folk Book*, was hugely informative and has been quoted from. Marjorie Bain and BBC Radio Shetland for the outstanding, and possibly unique recorded interview with Peerie Willie on *In Aboot Da Night*. Again, it has been mercilessly raided. Without John Graham's *Shetland Dictionary* and his and TA Robertson's *Grammar and Usage of the Shetland Dialect*, Mary Blance would have had an even harder job. John Hunter and Mary Smith were generous commissioners and editors. Thanks to Susan, for everything. And Shetland, for letting me stay.

I, however, take the blame for these words. As for much else.

Tom Morton is a journalist, author and broadcaster based in Northmavine. Previous publications include *Going Home: The Runrig Story*; *Spirit of Adventure*; *Hell's Golfer* and *Red Guitars in Heaven*. His latest novel, *Guttered*, is available from Mainstream Publishing.

SKINNER'S WAY

CALL me lucky; call it fate, call it carelessness. Call it divine providence, if you like. Truth to tell, there was a lot of incompetence and fortune involved in bringing me to these islands, and if God had a hand in it, well, I'll thank Him when or if we meet. And it won't be too long now, I think, before I make the final journey either to blessed blankness, or to face the Lord as He pores over my little life. In which case I'll have a bit of explaining to do. I suppose. I'll live, or indeed die, with that.

A thoughtless hand on the wheel, a bad decision over the amount of canvas we had aloft, or maybe it was indeed Our Father In Heaven who engineered the final gust of wind: anyway, I was hardly a youngster when the barque *Castlemaine*, heading for Lerwick out of Newcastle, loaded with pig-iron, collided with the Bard of Bressay in the early summer of 1875. I was 30 years old, second mate, off watch and swaying soundly in my hammock when a change in the sea's noise woke me. It was surf, crashing on a too-near shoreline; perhaps too there was a certain alteration in the ship's movement, the creak of her timbers. I was already scrambling on deck when the great rending, splintering judder told me we had foundered.

It had not been a pleasant voyage. The captain was a fat and fumbling inebriate, flame-faced and rheumy of eye on a shameless diet of biscuit and black Antigua rum, and the first mate, a ravaged Glaswegian, regarded me with a sly jealousy. I had taken the berth on a whim to fill in time - I was used to the coastal trade south of the Tyne, and the chance of a trip into the - for me - uncharted north was appealling. Besides, I had heard there was music in those northern islands we were bound for. 'Zetland' the Captain called them. He considered himself a modern, educated man. I preferred the softer, less Germanic 'Shetland', myself. Strange, for there were many islands in the group, and yet one word to cover them all. Later I was to discover that the original Norse word, *Hjaltland*, was singular, whereas the Orkneys and the Faroes both had plural roots. The singularity of Shetland as a place would become obvious to me in time.

In those days, I fancied myself as a bit of a hand on the button or squeezebox, the concertina as some proud souls sniffily call it. Northumbrian lad that I was, I had been reared on those cold hill reels and learned the trills and swinging lilts needed to send a chilled group of Saturday night dancers flailing across an earthen floor in our scattered hamlet's byre-dances.

The sea, even the English inshore trade, had brought

many additions to my repertoire, and I was sure Zetland would provide more. My much-loved Wheatstone was never far from me, but as I raced up the companionways to the deck that grim, pale night, mocking in its northern lightness, the instrument was far from my thoughts and securely locked in my cabin trunk.

Call it carelessness, call it luck, call it...the ability to swim.

In the tarns and pools high above Hexham I had learned to keep myself afloat, even to enjoy the refreshing summer dips in icy mountain water. But when the iron in her hold took the *Castlemaine* to the bottom, immersion in those Zetland seas was like a descent into a watery hell. The wind and swell were both running high, and the shock as I plunged beneath the waves was immense. Sour, salt liquid filled my nose and mouth. Somehow, I forced my limbs out of their paralysis, and as I surfaced, struck out for the dark shapes I hoped, prayed were the jumbled rocks of the shore. Any shore.

It took what seemed like hours. Music drifted through my mind as I battled the heavy, corkscrewing waves: fractured pieces of dry-land jigs and reels. For a time I was back in one of those byres with the packed-earth floors, flicking out *The Bonnie Geordie Lad Polka* to acclaim and the flashing, flirtatious eyes of beautiful girls. But excruciating agony dragged me back to the awful present. I had been smashed against an unyielding and jagged surface: rock. In that moment's pain was my salvation. I forced myself onto the low sea-battered outcrops after several failed attempts to do so, and slumped in cold exhaustion, conscious of a terrible throbbing pain in one hand. I had damaged it when that saving wave took me fiercely against the too-solid Shetland stone. Old Rock, they call the place, I know now. Aptly enough. Above me, a seemingly unclimbable cliff towered, black in the strange twilight and glimmered by thousands of luminous seabirds whose screeching combined with the gale to make an unearthly chorus.

It was there the Bressaymen found me, hoisted me, limp and unknowing, on the rope they used for egg collecting and retrieving fallen sheep, and gave me into the hands of the Manson family, the tender mercies of whose womenfolk brought me back to a semblance of health and strength. With the exception of my broken hand, the fingers of which never healed well enough to again hold a rope or finger the scales of a Northumbrian jig.

I was the only survivor from the *Castlemaine*. Those youthful episodes in the cold waters of my northern England home had brought me salvation, whereas my shipmates, holding almost certainly to that sailor's superstition that ability to swim is bad luck, had suffered the consequences. Such is the effect of irrational belief, in my opinion.

Somehow, like many a shipwrecked mariner before me, I stayed in the isles. Half crippled as I was, there seemed precious little but bad charity and chafing animal work awaiting me in the hills of home. The nursing of young Clemmie Manson led to a more emotional attachment between us, and through some of her father's political contacts - he was a zealous, radical liberal, and we delighted in many an argument on topics of the day - attempts were made to find me some kind of landlocked position. In the frenetic atmosphere of Lerwick at that time, which still largely continues even now, given the worldwide demand for fish and its plentiful supply in the neighbouring waters, there were opportunities in what they called, still call *da toon* for a young, rational man sea-trained, literate, as I thankfully was, and fairly numerate too. I found work in a shipping agents, and with Clemmie I settled into one of the old, narrow, tall houses behind the lodberries of the waterfront.

The Lord - there He is again; or fate, or whatever - did not bless us with children, but our lives were full; Clemmie had her family on Bressay and beyond, and there was the music, too. I could no longer play myself, but I had the chance to enjoy what I discovered truly was a community blessed with the twin gifts of rhythm and melody.

I say that, but to be exact, it is a gift of... enjoyment. Never, in my youthful dalliances in the hills and dales of Northumbria, have I encountered such a fierce desire to celebrate the sheer fact of life, of being alive. A hunger, eagerness for joy, for light in the omnipresent winter darkness. And I admit, in those younger days, when I was gripped with a wild love of existence, of being saved from the cold depths of the ocean, I participated in that fierce rejoicing, sometimes to excess. The Unst bere-ale, and the fire water illicitly distilled from it....ah well. The less said the better. I preferred the rum or Geneva spirits brought in from Dutch vessels lying off Bressay, deep in the blackness of moonless winter nights. But it does not do, even nowadays, to talk too openly of such things.

Music, it seemed, was for and about dancing, and many was the long cold journey Clemmie and I, usually with one or other of her brothers or sisters in tow, would take my horse and cart to an isolated waterfront shed, say in Voe or once, even to an ancient hostelry in Hillswick. There to find one, sometimes two fiddlers, fiercely sawing out wild tunes of an intensely rhythmic nature it was hard, nay impossible to ignore. They spoke, sang to your body, forced you to dance.

And Clemmie delighted in kicking my clumsy feet into the correct shapes. Poor Clemmie. How she loved to dance.

They played, these fiddlers, the Strathspeys and reels I was familiar with from my seafaring and shore leaves, even some of the rough countryside overtones of Northumbria, Scotland and Ireland. But there were older tunes, some of them named for the mythical creatures known as trows or trowies, and these had a fierce, dark magical air, albeit with an edge of hysteria. Some old men told me tales of two-stringed fiddle-like instruments, reaching back to those ancient trowie days, for they say the trows were really the little dark Picts pillaged and harried by the raiding and then settling Vikings. Who can be certain?

Some players, particularly those whose roots were in the outer islands of Yell, Papa Stour, Fetlar and Whalsay, used a tuning I was unacquainted with, but which I was told had great similarities to the Norwegian style of playing. Once, an old man unpacked an ancient oversized instrument, bigger even than a viola, and I was astounded to note that it had two extra drone strings which rang and resonated in a most appealling manner, adding depth and texture to the dancing accompaniment. If only there had been some means of preserving these different sounds, styles and the many tunes, such as the one melody played throughout the isles with varying degrees of skill and in a range of local styles: *Da Hen's March to da Midden*, as the sly wit of the Shetlanders has it. That and another humorously named item, *Da Soo's Lament for Tatties*....ah yes, I can hear them ringing in my head even now, now that I am old, and in the style of perhaps 30 different players. Strangely, there was little singing; a few fragments of old Norse songs, one or two humorous ditties on the subject of the crofter's hardships. Tales, though were told, magical, often supernatural stories linked to the rugged landscape and its shoreline border with the endless ocean. Music, however, tended to be left to stand alone. The elemental truths of a great tune were perhaps thought to make words irrelevant and unnecessary.

Sometimes I look back on my, what is it, 40 odd years now in Shetland - Zetland, as the Government is seemingly keen for the place to be termed - and I can hardly believe the speed and extent of change. True, there are still many sailing vessels coming and going, but steam and coal have together usurped the whimsical wind which brought me here in the first place, and destroyed all my shipboard companions. And then there is The War, the one people are now calling The Great War, the likes of which it is almost impossible for me to accept that I have lived through, albeit as an elderly bystander. Clemmie, God - there He is again - rest her soul, did not

19

survive me, or The War. A shameful thing, that, her having helped save me in the first place from the chilling deep. Sometimes I think knowledge, such as we had, of what was going on in the trenches killed her.

But the melody, the dancing, the life continued. The War brought soldiers, new faces, bodies, voices; new styles, new tunes, new sounds and rhythms impregnated the wondrous mongrel Shetland music with something new, something old, something strange. It was a heady business - and a sly secret I kept to myself - hearing tunes which I could identify, more slowly as I grew older, as Dutch, even Canadian. And little snippets of Maypole-dancing English- ness would creep in to some unsuspecting Scalloway man's bowing, about which I of course would say nothing. Though I confess to shedding a tear or two when I heard an old Northumbrian air played, so many years and miles from the hill farms in which I had heard it last, had played it indeed, when I had the use of both my hands.

The coming of the gramophone - I pride myself that I had one of the first in the islands - brought the mystery of recorded music into my home, better furnished as the years went by and my worth was recognised ever more profitably by my employers. Something in me yearned, yearns to have the fast disappearing abilities of all those elderly island fiddlers placed on fragile black discs. As if such a thing were possible! But anyway, it is too late for too many of them.

Nevertheless, music from Scotland, England, even America came in permanent, stored form, and across the islands, seeped into the brains and fingers of local players. I gaze at my broken, twisted, scarred right hand sometimes and feel it itching. Cold and excessive damp these days sends arrows of agony shooting from it up my arm; I can feel the rough kiss of that Bressay rock: so much gained, and so much lost.

The tall house is too big and chilly for me now, too many stairs, and to be honest I expect to slip down one cold winter's morning and let a snapped hip carry me onward and upward to the great darkness or the huge and eternal light, whichever it is. All my life I have expected nothing when I die. Somehow, uncertainty is creeping in. Age brings weakness, I suppose. Age has also brought a loss of opportunity to hear music in the further reaches of the islands, though one or two of my surviving friends occasionally cosset and coddle me to such adventurous outposts as Cunningsburgh or even Gott. To tell the truth, my old bones do not like it. Rheumatism has crept in, and the shiver of that far distant night in the waters of Bressay Sound sometimes reaches from my mangled hand through my whole being like....like a hint of imminent death.

But there is still Blind George, and the music of the streets, still life. He is not alone, George, George Stark from Dundee, in his performing for the hordes of workers who still throng Lerwick in the cause of the silver fish, the great herring. Other musicians glean a meagre living from the generosity and sentimental homesickness of the fish-workers. But he has been coming every summer now since... well. For quite a long time. Fifteen, 16 years, maybe; his playing is a small dance of joy to me in my twilight years, these dimming days.

Often I will settle myself on the pierhead, outside the steamer store, or at the Market Cross, and if it is a fine day, wallow in the strains of his bow-work, so oddly formal compared to the variegated wildnesses I have heard in these islands. In my time.

Once I listened to him playing a tune, a great, sprightly piece called, I think, *The Bonnie Lass o' Bon Accord*, one that had all the hallmarks of the great Strathspey formalist Scott Skinner, whose tunes had spread like wild-fire across Scotland and beyond, and certainly to Shetland. I could not help but approach him with congratulations.

"My" he said with that insight the sightless often have

"that's a right mongrel of accents. A seaman sir? But maybe not for a whiley?"

"Not for many years, Mr Stark" I replied. By then, my Northumbrian vowels had been overlaid with the 'dees' and 'dus' of Zetlandic dialect, with its quaint Norse terms and great colourful words based around the multiple rhythms and melodies of daily life. "Tell me, that tune, *The Bonnie Lass o' Bon Accord* - I would guess that to be a Skinner piece?"

His great face, with those terribly blank eyes, broke into a smile and he seemed to be communicating with another time, a happy, dark and sightless memory.

"There's a story there, sir" he said "yes, a tale worth the telling." And he stopped. His accomplice, and guide, a smaller man, raised his eyebrows at me, and of course I rummaged in my pocket for a coin or two to ease the communication, never minding that I had already popped more than the one penny into that proferred cap.

"Aye" said George, on hearing the chink of coinage on cloth "aye, a tale right enough, and it's this. Once I was playing that very tune in Aberdeen, on Union Street. You ken it, sir, perhaps?" And I had to say that no, I did not, that despite my profession as shipping agent and the time I had spent in Shetland, I had never set sail again, other than the occcasional flit boat crossing to Yell, and of course Bressay.

It was not so much fear, as the presence of an unavoidable physical barrier, just beyond the Sooth Mooth. The sea had cast me here, and I could not leave. Not that I bothered the Blind Fiddler with this tale. My marooned state was my own concern.

"Anyway, there I was, sawing away at my old fiddle in the midst of the Union Street crowds, *The Bonnie Lass O' Bon Accord*, right enough, a favourite of the loons and quines in the siller city, and there's a tap on my shoulder. 'Can ye no' play it right?' comes a voice. And I stop, because I have my pride, sir, you understand, and modesty forbids, but there are those who say I had then a dod o' skill on the old rosined strings. And doubtless I was a wee bit annoyed, for I said, maybe a bit gruff-like: 'What? Who in the name of the wee man are you to tell me, me who's been playing this tune for years, that it's no right? It's as right as bloody rain, man, and if you can do any better, then you can tak that fiddle and do it your bloody self. Wha do you think you are, you cheeky so and so?'"

"My name's Skinner" he said "and I wrote yon piece, my friend." Then he took the fiddle oot o' my hands, and there they were, the notes I'd been playing, but man, you've never heard the like of it. Sweet. Sweet and awfy hard, and singing, like....a church bell, or the bones in woman's face... Forgive me sir. I'm getting fanciful; carried away, but well, you'll be wanting your money's worth!"

We all laughed at that: me, his companion and the Blind Fiddler himself.

"Well, then. He finishes playing, and I hears a burst of applause from the crowd that's gathered, the sound of coins going in my titfer. And my Goad, It's right enough himself, Scott Skinner, his fingers on my fiddle. And I'll say this...." he paused. It was an oft-told tale, clearly. "He almost got the damned thing right. Almost!"

And our expected, but genuine laughter merged with the screech of the gulls, taking me back shivering to a stormy June night beneath a cliff across the sound, many years before.

Sometimes my mind wanders, deposits me in places I had no intention of revisiting. I think to the days before I came here, to the family, such as it was, I have abandoned in those Northumbrian hills. I did of course, write to inform them of my safety, and sent money regularly to my mother and the brood of sisters who continued the mountain life we had lived for generations. Sometimes notes would come back written by the local priest on my illiterate siblings' behalf, doubtless at the cost of some of the money I sent. They were bland, short, missives from a lost way of life, and finally they stopped. Curiosity about the past ebbed away as I immersed myself in my Shetland existence, exchanged the thrill of strangeness for normality, for acceptance.

Lately, however, I catch myself in a reverie of nostalgia, and sometimes I wish I could make one last journey back to that North of England landscape, with is lack of sea, with its trees, rocks and jagged horizons.

But the other day I saw and heard something which drove all such maudlin morbidities out of my mind. I had taken a seat on one of the stone benches at the Market Cross, for I knew that George Stark was to play there, and it was a fine, sunny June day, with little wind. My old bones could handle the cold rock beneath my ever-bonier buttocks for an hour or two. And maybe The Blind Fiddler would play *The Bonnie Lass o' Bon Accord*. Often he would say hallo to me, without a word having come from my lips. Somehow he could tell when I was there. Maybe I had developed a distinctive old man's aroma, a scent. I hope not. But it is, after all, one of the regrettable aspects of ageing.

George was playing away, this time with his friend Willie Jordan on scratchy guitar, a recent innovation, and too loud and aggressive for my tastes, I must say. Who knows where it will lead, this kind of introduction? But then, age may be making its intolerant presence felt. Suddenly I became aware of a small lad, clearly smartened up for a day in "da toon", and probably from a fairly distant rural area. He was wearing one of the traditional gansies, a tweed jacket, long short trousers and his legs were scabbed and battered. He was a substantial little fellow, or peerie boy as they say, grave and solid between two casual bystanders, but all his concentration was on the Blind Fiddler. It was a collision between blindness and sight. Briefly I worried that George would be consumed by the child's terrifyingly concentrated, almost greedy gaze.

I sat, an old man, invisible to George, and certainly to the boy, who had eyes only for the flying fingers of the Blind Fiddler. And to everyone else, too, as I was part of the street, old and familiar enough to merge, almost, with the stones, like flotsam on the shore.

Presently a man came up, clearly the boy's father, dressed in the style of a fisherman. He put his hand on the boy's shoulder, but there was determination there in the child, very nearly an anger. I could hear the conversation quite clearly, conducted in the dialect of, at a guess, the northern district called Northmavine. I reproduce it here as best I can. I remember that George had just played *The Banks Hornpipe*, and the boy had grown excited; I could see his fingers twitching. A tyro musician, I realised, a boy like I had been

27

once, consumed with the possibilities represented by this old blind man. A boy whose world had just opened up into the realisation that endless creative space was waiting to be explored, just through a trip into town and the sound of a visiting, frankly past his best, fiddler.

"Com du" said the father "du's heard enoff."

"Na na" came the reply. "I'm no' goin. I'm no goin' at a. I'm bidin' here."

The father had the look of a man whose dealings with his children were rare. He was probably more used to the companionship of the sea, and left matters of domestic discipline to his wife at home. There was a kind of gentle confusion in his eyes.

"Weel" he said "I hae ta go and get some messages to send up ta dee midder." I realised he was probably based here in Lerwick for the summer's fishing, with his family far away, and that this was a special trip by his son into town to see him. I wondered at how rejected he might feel, at his son's passion for the Blind Fiddler as opposed to the man who was his rarely-seen parent.

"Dat's aaright" said the boy "just laeve me whaar I am." The man stood in silence. I could have wept for him as he sought the words to reach out to his son.

"Haes du ony money?" he asked at last.

"I hae tippence" came the reply.

"Na na" said the man, shaking his head. "dat's nae use...here."

And, delving into a leather bag he had attached to his belt, he handed over a clutch of coins, too much, with all the heartbroken, heartbreaking generosity of a man striving to make contact, blunderingly. "When he comes aroon...gie him wan o dat, an dunna be cheeky, jist gie him dat, pit hit in." And then, hesitating, wondering, uncertain, the man left the boy standing there so sure of himself and rapt with attention, yet unseen by the blind man.

Something leapt into my throat, made me speak when normally I would have kept silent. "Here George" I said, knowing he would recognise my tortured mixture of accents "play us da *Hyltadance*."

"Ach, the old trowie tunes" said George "when you could be having the civilised Strathspeys of Perthshire, or the delicate works of Neil Gow. I don't know..." I jingled the coins in my pocket, subtly, you understand so as not to insult. Willie Jordan walked over with his old cloth cap and I put a silver threepeenny piece in. Soon the old Shetland tune, one of the oldest in fact, was hurtling from the deceptively contained movements of the old fiddler. True, he did not play it as some of the elderly men locally still did, holding the fiddle against their chests. But he had caught the flavour, if not the rough, ringing style of the best native players.

When he had finished, Willie was walking around with his cap, picking up a penny here and there, and he was set to walk past the little lad when the boy put two of his father's hard-earned ha'pennies into the receptacle and said, in his suprisingly deep voice:

"Please sir, wid ye axe da fiddler ta play da *Banks's Hornpipe* agin?"

Willie looked at him for a moment, then shrugged. Soon the familiar strains of that tune, another of Skinner's little masterpieces, were resounding along the street. George played it twice, and when the cap went around, the boy jingled in another two ha'pennies, and again demanded the same tune. And a third time. The few bystanders who had stayed throughout George's performance were laughing quietly to themselves, and George himself clearly felt he had played it enough.

"Wha is it who's wanting this same old tune all of the time?" he demanded. "Is someone trying to steal it aff me, eh?"

"Och" said Willie "there's a wee loon down here keeps asking for it."

"Fetch him up here, and let's hae a wee look at him"

said George. He was never one to take his own disability so seriously that he couldn't make a joke about it himself, though heaven help anyone else who punned his lack of power to see. There was a scattered round of applause as the boy was hauled over to George, who crouched down and demanded:

"Where did you hear yon tune?" The lad, hugely embarrassed, stared down at the great flagstones of the street, and mumbled.

"Louder, boy" boomed George "I may be blind, but I didnae think I was geein deef as weel!"

"Aff a record" said the boy, clearly now "A gramophone record."

"I see" said George, the old joker, or maybe he just wasn't thinking about what he was saying. "Wha was playin on them?"

"Skinner" said the boy, with an odd kind of familiarity, as if he was an old professional confidant or colleague of the great man.

"Aye aye" said George "Jamie Scott Skinner. I ken that record weel. Just as I kent him weel, tae." Which was embroidering things a bit, I considered. "Dae ye ken onything else on that record?"

"Whit? lik... is it *Arthur's Seat*?"

"Aye, lad, that's richt." And without another word,

George stood up and burst into the self-same *Arthur's Seat*. Not too shabbily, in my opinion; I too possess the bakelite disc concerned. When he'd finished the boy, now standing right in front of George, asked what key he was playing in, and suddenly the two were in a crouched discussion of technique. The boy had the fiddle in his hands, and was carefully, and accurately playing a scale, the same scale as the last tune, probably an E flat. For a few minutes the pair were lost in the business of making the instrument do what the boy was demanding of it. It was clear that the lad had more than talent. There was something both innately skilled and utterly determined about him.

"Du's still here, boy?"

It was the father, the fisherman, back and watching the strangely contrasting figures, one bulkily adult, awkwardly on his hunkers by the boy, large for a child, but still small. "He's no botherin dee, sir, is he?"

"Nah, nah" said George. "He seems keen on learning, and I'd always encourage that, absolutely."

"Can I no bide a peerie bit langer, faither?" The boy was not pleading, so much as stating what was going to happen. And the father, shrugging, as if the mystery of his son had slipped beyond him, and he was somehow admitting that, said quietly:

"Weel, maybe I can leave dee anidder 20 minutes or sae while I get some mair errands, as lang as du's aaright?"

"I'm fine" said the boy, his eyes on the unseeing eyes of the Blind Fiddler "fine, fine fine."

George performed another few sets of tunes, and then he and the boy ran over some more scales, and the youngster played him his version of the *Banks Hornpipe*. It was in a different key from the one George used, and made me feel most peculiar. Most of the time, when I heard the Shetlanders playing their music, it took me part of the way back to some half-forgotten part of the islanders' past: some snatch of lore or legend I had been told, through the mists, perhaps of ale or spirits.

But when this boy played, it sounded like a way to the future. A bridge between what had gone before and what was still to come.

It was time for me to go home. I could feel the bitter shroud of Bressay Sound lapping, flapping around me, and as I hauled myself up on my old stick, I could hear the click and snap of wasted muscle and worn-out legs and arms. Back in the emptiness of my silent, cold, tall house, I could fill the lonely hours with music, scratchy recordings on the gleaming horn gramophone. Scott Skinner himself would be my companion. What a pity, I thought that no-one had

recorded the things I had heard, the magical tunes which would probably be lost forever.

As I moved slowly down Commercial Street towards home, I heard the boy, the scale fully mastered, fingering the *Banks Hornpipe*, again, this time in George's key. And suddenly I felt reassured. Maybe the music of these islands I had grown to love would have a future after all. A future where the past would not be forgotten.

God would know. When I see Him, I will ask Him.

SCHENECTADY CALLING

1: Wireless

RONAS Hill glowed a ragged red in the distance, as the tall young man festooned lengths of wire around the crofthouse on the Stenness road, for all the world like a washing line, or as if he was about to decorate Lower Heogland with fairy lights.

It was a late summer evening, and the sun was hovering like a badly-healed wound out in the Atlantic by the time he had finished. Inside, the crystal set completed that afternoon lay neatly attached to a piece of driftwood he had planed and sawed until it could have come from Hay's. The end of the wire which was waving gently outside in what was hardly a breeze by Shetland standards, he attached to the two terminals. The battered headphones, salvaged from who knew what shipwreck, he placed over his ears. And gently, softly, as if he was dealing with a valuable musical instrument, the large young man began tuning the brass needle across the copper coil, prowling the airwaves. He was 19, and he was reeling the world in to Eshaness.

"It was 1929...at I took a coorse in wireless. I was 19 dan, and it wis a postal coorse. I began ta build sets, and in fact I hid a

good business goin. I designed my own sets for dis kind of climes. It was a great thrill at the time, but it did a lot of harm as well as good, because the aald men at heard dis, dey packed up da fiddle. They felt they couldna play like dis, du sees. Not in da ootlyin places laek da country, but in da toon it wis rapidly a bad thing. An I look back on it an regret in some wyes at dey wir sae much o dat, an we didna hae, der wisna some kind o primitive recordings o da Shetland thing....because dey wir so much lost...."

The tall young man has a fiddle in his hand, now, and crouched with him over a large, clearly home-made valve radio is a small, intense figure, crowned with a mound of wavy, brilliantined, combed hair. From the huge cardboard-and-wax speaker comes a wave of static and hiss, but in the midst is melody, a music both sweet and bitter, smooth and syncopated, alien and familiar. An announcer's voice, American, honeyed, moneyed, fades back and forth. Gulls are shrieking outside, on the roofs and windowsills of Lerwick, and sometimes they drown the wireless's limited volume.

"Schenectady calling, Schenectady calling....this is the American Armed Forces Radio Network, broadcasting live from the stage at Schenectady, New York State, USA, and

that was Joe Venuti, on violin, accompanied by Eddie Lang, guitar...."

As the shrieking of the seabirds reaches a crescendo, the bigger of the two men switches off the wireless, and hoists his fiddle under his chin. "I dinna ken, Willie," he mutters. "It's affil fine, but du canna pit it wi wir stuff here, da aald stuff. Dat Joe Venuti's excellent, but hoo wid he cope wi da Eshaness dance band, howking accordions on da back of motorbikes, eh? Dos du tink him and dat Eddie Lang wid survive a Whalsay wedding?"

The smaller man grins, crouches low over his guitar, and plays a bewildering run of chords, complete with bass lines mysteriously fretted by a bent thumb.

"Ach, Willie" says the taller man. "Keep it simple, for the love of God."

"I had to keep it very basic at first with Tom, nothing fancy, because he wanted it that way. In any case, you can't put a lot of thirteenths and flattened fifths into Shetland reels. It takes away from it, in my opinion. You try to keep it the way it's supposed to be, and that's the way Tom liked it."

Many years and a world war later, the fiddler and the

guitarist, relaxed in each other's company, are playing *Lady Mary Ramsay*, the guitarist wickedly sneaking in some dazzling jazz runs in a way which still, after all this time, draws a furrowed brow and muttered swearing from his companion. When they stop, the guitarist rises from his chair to close the outside door, which is swinging open.

"Just leave it, Willie" says the fiddler, loosening a button on his waistcoat. "Dere's a peerie boy lives next door liks tae come in by and hear da fiddle." And sure enough, a few minutes later, a sturdily built child pokes his head around the door as the two musicians skitter their way nonchalently through a set of reels. When they stop, the fiddler nods to the boy. "Dis" he says "dis is Aly." The bairn hunkers down on the floor in front of the fiddle player, his eyes round with admiration, his mouth agape. "Is du gyaan tae play da fiddle when du's aalder, dan, Aly?" But the boy says nothing.

"It was Willie who took Eddie Lang's chords and his own chords and put them to fiddle music, and of course they fitted perfectly. It's the same rhythm we have now on piano - we call it 'dumchick' because that's the way the rhythm goes. Willie has a genius for working out chords. In fact, he figured them all out on piano first and then transposed the chords to the guitar. He introduced tenths, ninths, thirteenths and

flattened fifths - all the things the jazzmen were playing - and he passed them on to the next generation of Shetland pianists, Ronnie Cooper and Violet Tulloch."

Now the peerie boy is grown up, long haired, bearded, but still sturdy. It is 1979, and he is famous. But the tall young fiddler and the dapper little guitarist of his childhood still figure large in his life, albeit shaped, like himself, rather differently by the intervening years. Now they are beside him, on a huge stage, seated on cheap plastic chairs. The tall young man who once brought crystal radio sets to the North Mainland of Shetland is heavier now, bespectacled and bald; he is wearing a strange combination of smart leather brogues, glittering in the stage lights, neatly pressed flannel trousers, and a Boys of the Lough T-shirt. But the fiddle held to his neck is as natural a part of his body as an arm or a leg. Aly, the peerie boy of yore, wears Cuban-heeled cowboy boots and flared jeans. Slightly apart is the guitarist, bearing an alarming resemblance to the new wave rock star Elvis Costello in a tight dark suit, glasses and helmet of crinkly hair, his Pearl acoustic guitar held at an acute angle to his body, his chin resting on the edge of the instrument. A large and enthusiastic crowd cheer the music coming from the various combinations of players on the vast stage. At one point, the guitarist leans across to the older fiddler and whispers:

"Aye Tammy. Dos du tink da ghost of Eddie Lang is here? Is Joe Venuti peeking ower dy shooder?". But the expression on the big old man's face does not change.

"Fir Christ's sake Willie" he says "keep it simple, man. Where dos du think du is? Schenectady?" And they look at each other, the ghost of a grin playing around the fiddler's lips, then out at the crowd of Americans beyond the footlights, at the old concert hall with its superb acoustics. And they wonder, briefly, about how things are in the Lounge, Lerwick. And whether there any good bars in Schenectady, New York State, where they can get a tune after the show.

(2) Da Sooth Boat

Leaving was hard, but it was something he'd been born with, like the men who went deep sea, or to the whaling: there was a restlessness, a need to do more than see the world; to prove yourself against it.

But when you left Shetland, obeying the call of the sea, you were following a well-trodden pathway, joining a respected community of temporary expatriates. This was different. What he was doing was setting himself apart, saying not that he was better, but that he was different, and that, yes, maybe he was as good as he could ever be if he stayed where he was. That he needed new challenges, new inspirations. Needed to go out there and find the music, engage with it, rather than sit at the crossroads of the northern oceans and wait for it to come to him.

After all, wasn't that what both Willie and Tammy had done? True, they had been presented with the opportunity by the war, but look at the benefits it had brought them. There was Tammy, capable of waxing lyrical about the 24-note scale found in Indian music, having spent two and a half years of the war listening to bloody sitars, for God's sake; or Willie, playing with some of the best jazz dancebands in Europe, courtesy of contacts made at Sullom Voe, of all places, and then in bars scattered the length and breadth of Britain.

They had brought their treasures home, shed their hard-won lustre on younger musicians growing up. On him. And he was leaving, unsure if he'd ever come back.

Competitive. He'd always been like that, wanting to win. It was in his attitude towards his trade of joinery, towards the racquet games he'd played so well. But there was also a sense of the wider world that he'd known from a very early age was uncommon among the boys he grew up with, later worked and played alongside. Politics. He'd been brought up to think for himself, to believe in the universal equality of

43

mankind; the superiority of no-one. He not only had that untypically Shetlandic self-belief, but the communism of his parents had given him a world view, not just an island outlook. He wanted to be part of that bigger existence. Embrace it.

In some ways, he knew he could never come back. He'd seen the ones who'd failed, who'd left to follow their skill, their dream, had slunk back into the isles to be welcomed, on the face of it, as if they'd never been away. Apart from the occasional mild piece of sarcasm which you could see felling the sorry victim like an axe.

He would never put himself through that. He had too much pride. But he realised too that success would be a mixed blessing for the people who knew him in the islands. Some would rejoice, would have their hearts lifted, would see that Shetland was benefitting by his rise to fame, by his increasing skill; that as he was recognised, so the isles which had spawned him would be.

Others would feel weakened, diminished, jealous. He could hear them now: "Aye, he's no bad, but he canna play a slow air lik...."

"Did du hear he smashed his fiddle up when he heard yon peerie boy, how much better as him he was?"

"Ach, he's too big for wis, noo. Too big for his ain seaboots...."

He'd already had a taste of that, with his trips sooth. Failure and success. Had returned with his tail between his legs, lonely and frightened. But still hadn't given up, had forced his face against that eternal grindstone again and again, driven by something, maybe some old Viking spirit, some need to conquer. And then, as people in Glasgow and Edinburgh began to appreciate his playing, he would come back to quiet comments in the bar: "Is du no at Carnegie Hall ee noo?" One day, he thought to himself, laughing along with the rest, quietly. One day.

Sooth, they had occasionally laughed at him. He remembered one ill-conceived audition for some godless variety show on TV. He'd come straight down with a salmon as a gift for someone, and for whatever reason it was strapped to his fiddle case. They'd laughed then, offered to buy the fish, but not him.

One day.

He had to go. Yes, he'd be back, but the life, the living, the absolute belonging was over. From now on he would always be part of Shetland, but apart from it. Travelling, yes. Getting better. He felt that fiercely. Collecting new ideas, new techniques, testing himself against the best. He was going where there were no limits. Where he could find out if he was the best, and there was no shame in thinking, just thinking,

you might be.

It was time to go. The *St Clair's* whistle sounded like the wrath of God over Lerwick, rattling the bottles on the gantry of The Lounge, crowded with imminently departing passengers.

"Gie's a tune, boy" said someone as he stood up, resolute, nervous, exultant with what mysteries might lie in front of him. He looked sideways at the man who had spoken. An old workmate, face prematurely bloated and broken-veined with booze. "Gie's a tune, ya bastard. A tune for wis poor sods left behind."

Carefully, he placed the fiddle case on the bar, took out the instrument, and began tuning it. The room's chatter and row hushed; the few musicians around the piano stopped. Everyone looked at him, expectant. And suddenly he laughed.

"Gie me anidder dram, Hughie." There was just time to get on board the boat yet. And he began to play. For The Lounge, the man with the raddled face, for Lerwick, for the world. For himself, too. And for the future.

(3) How?

"That's one of the great things about Aly, he's given Shetland

musicians exposure. And by his own example, he's encouraged Shetlanders not to be so inward looking. Shetlanders never wanted to go to the mainland. They didn't want to try anything new. But Aly has encouraged them to go, and he has given them their chance."

"I played with a lot of the old Shetland fiddlers, donkey's years ago, and it was all Shetland style. But it was slower than they play it now. That's how they got the lift in their playing. Very few fiddlers do it now. Aly does it. And Willie Hunter could. And Davie Tulloch. That slower stuff was what Tammy was trying to collect.

I used to play the guitar fast, but you can't get the lift if you play too fast. Aly can do it. He's got it kind of perfected that he can play all these things and get the tone and the lift, even when there's speed. He kind of digs into it. He's aye got... the life. A lot of fiddlers play it pretty straight, to the book, no matter how good a tone they've got. Aly's got more life in it."

It was a hard tour, but the fiddler, who was in his sixties, and the guitarist, who wasn't that much younger, took it in their stride.

"Soft drinks only" said the fiddler.

"That'll be gin and tonic then?"

"Aye. Make it a pint."

The guitarist had played with some of the best British jazzateers during and after the war, and nothing, nobody could intimidate him. Some, however, could astonish. Like the star-struck chambermaid who knocked on his hotel room door to be faced with an undressed, middle-aged Shetlander, fresh from his bleary bed.

"Excuse me sir" she said, "are you an artist?" Instantly, he realised he was. Even though what he actually said to her was "Aye, a piss artist."

An artist, though? An artiste, maybe. He'd heard that term used often enough in the dancehalls of London and the home counties after the war. What was he, exactly? A laundryman who got lucky? What?

A Yell man, to begin with, reared in Lerwick, with a father buried in Jamaica. He wondered about that, his memories of the man who had died when he was seven. He could only remember having seen him once, "atween boats". It was like a photograph, a snatch of film.

He had been ill, terribly ill during his childhood, confined to bed on one occasion for nearly nine months. He'd heard that was true, strangely enough, of many... artists. The scarlet fever had nearly killed him. Then there was the asthma, the measles. But it was the scarlet fever that had turned his attention to the guitar. For some reason the *News of the World* had printed a series of ukelele chords. Probably the most useful thing that rag had ever done. And then his cousin had been making a kind of a guitar, and what with the music, the old 78's around the house, Scott Skinner, Harry Lauder, country and western, what they called hillbilly then....well. It had just seemed natural to try and play along.

Then there was the 30 bob guitar his mother had scrimped and saved for, the Len Williams chord book; Len Williams - father of the classical fellow, John Williams. Maybe John, too, had known all the chords, or nearly all of them, had worked them out for himself. Sitting listening to records seamen and his cousins had brought, some from America, black bakelite, brittle, unbelievably precious; and the radio, the wireless, hauling in treasure from the depths of the ether. Fishing for tunes.

The feeling when he first heard Reinhardt, those chords, and him with hardly a whole hand on the left. Grapelli, the fiddle. A possibility tingling away at the back of his mind. Sitting in the darkness of the sitting room, trying to work out what the hell the man was doing. That sudden flash of inspiration, realising what a flattened fifth was, how it was built, like a piece of...sculpture maybe. Call that artistry if you wanted. More like brickwork.

Working as a message boy, in a drapers, still playing away, still trying to get better, but not really knowing why, what for. Just because it felt good, felt right. Then one day, maybe about 16, seeing this huge bloke walk into that music shop next to Pottingers, his cousin nudging the enormous figure, and saying, aye boy, here's a guitarist'll play wi' you. When was that? 1936? About then. All the battles, all the delight, all the good and bad...you could date it from that day. Now, the big man was an artist. Knew it too. Wasn't afraid to let folk now, either.

Ah, but once it had been the two of them, Billy Kay, one or two others, playing in halls all over the place, finding that people wanted to hear, that he could make the fiddle sing better than it could alone, just with his strumming.

Was it one moment, or a gradual realisation? Sitting there, with the big fiddler, listening to the radio, to the Schenectady broadcasts. Hearing Eddie Lang, and thinking, I can do this. He's making Joe Venuti sing like a bird. I can do that with the big man, with other fiddlers too. Reinhardt with Grapelli. No matter we don't play jazz. Jazz is a state of mind. Everything I play, that's jazz. Somebody had a record, and he kept playing it, listening to the Lang spaces, the feel, the lift, the life.

Turning those flattened fifths into something Scottish, something Shetland: it could be done. It was obvious, really. Just thanking his lucky stars that they didn't play the bag-pipes in the isles, otherwise how would those jazz chords have fitted? Christ, it would have been a shambles. It was one of the key things about Shetland fiddle, he realised. The bloody bagpipes had never affected it, made it squeal and shriek.

Getting the bass runs as well as the chords, using that old thumb, until it was done and dusted, a style.

An art? No. Not really. A craft, maybe. *Eddie Lang*, he used to tell people. *Blame him.* Now he was an artist. Died young, left a legacy. Leaving something for others, though, that was the thing. Maybe.

"There was nobody really playing here in Shetland when I started. I had to teach myself. Nowadays, people ask me about chords, and I tell them they have to figure it out for themselves. When Tammy taught his pupils, everything had to be correct, the way he played it. I like to encourage them to play something different, so I try to put them on the road and give them the basics, and then they can take off on their own from there."

The war scattered them. The fiddler had gone to Northern Ireland, then India, something to do with radar. And for himself, there was the RAF.

In uniform, heading south. The train journey to Leith, waking up from a whisky-fuelled sleep in the middle of the Forth Bridge, to find a bombing raid in progress, in-cendiaries going off. Head out of the window, lost in the spectacle of it, until a passing red cap hauled him in and almost put him on a charge for breaking the blackout. The war was there. Here.

Wiltshire, Bournemouth and then, of all things, posted back to Shetland, to the seaplane base at Sullom Voe.

Fifteen blokes in a hut, playing music for all they were worth. Even a peerie Italian prisoner of war, smiling, crying, desperate to play. They'd smuggled him in. The war scattered music. And musicians as well, with members of bands like Ambrose's and Roy Fox's formed into small units for entertaining the troops. And they came to Shetland, where he would ask to sit in with them, showing them a trick or two, on bass or guitar, when they thought he was just some local yokel. *Eddie Lang*, he would say; *blame him*. Boy, said one worse-for-wear drummer, you've got a good ear. Best I've ever come across. You're an artist, man.

Caddington in 1946, getting ready for demob. Every-thing, the world, getting ready to change, and there he was in

London, taking the tube to see a cousin, and there's a poster advertising a band; the leader's name familiar - one of the guy's he'd sat in with at Sullom Voe. Nothing ventured, nothing gained. Off he went to Muswell Hill, just on the off chance, to say hallo. Next thing, he's sitting in with this top flight London band. Turns into a regular thing. Then he's demobbed, 1947, still enjoying himself, playing here, there and everywhere and to be honest the details become a bit vague. Big halls, 1000 people, maybe more, and he's taking solos, right at the front of the band, everybody watching. One night Vera Lynn - was it her, really? Was she ever coming? - doesn't turn up, and he has to do a party piece. Great days.

Auditions he didn't care for, unpleasant people. Chances missed, no question, but you picked and you chose, made your own luck. An offer to join a band, full-time, good money. But he was enjoying himself too much the way things were, jumping from gig to gig, relaxed. Then a serious opportunity: a six month contract in France, with Joe Daniels. But he wasn't feeling well, by this time. Needing to get home. And just like that, he made his way north, north until the land ran out, and then north again. Home.

"I was in London with Willie Hunter in 1958, and I went to see a pal of mine, a guitar player called Chick Lovell. Went to

speak to him, and he said he'd got started with a band when this Scotch bloke never turned up. And that was me, that was the band I'd been playing in. So he went to France, then on to Italy, and he met Marlene Deitrich, became her guitar player for 11 years..."

Home then, and back into the swing of things, once he was feeling that bit better. And still the call of the outside world, the big stages: The Festival Hall, once, with Shuldham Shaw. Folk festivals, and more and more, over the years, people coming and saying that his guitar style was spreading across the world, how did he do that bass run thing with his thumb, could he give this American a wee lesson, did he fancy a sweet sherry and a game of pool? *Eddie Lang*, he would grin: *blame him*. And Aly. A lot of those gigs sooth, all that television work; that was his fault.

Now this: a fun, no question, but daft. That business in San Francisco, he and Tammy at it like cat and dog over who had seen the biggest Redwood tree, for God's sake. Here in Juneau, though, it's early, and neither Tammy nor Aly is anywhere to be seen. Time to find a bar, maybe.

So into this place, looks fine, dark and absolutely full of.. Indians. Bit threatening at first, but soon enough everyone starts yarning away, a lot of them work on the Alaska Pipelines, they know all about Shetland, Sullom Voe, the oil thing. After a peerie start, one or two drinks, out he comes, runs slap bang into Aly and Tammy, both of them frantic looking for him, turns out this bar is an Indians only joint, dangerous for white men. Off limits.

"Du's not supposed to geng in dere" says the bigger of the two fiddlers.

The guitarist just looks at the two of them, grins and raises the flat of one hand in a salute he remembers seeing Tonto give the Lone Ranger:

"How!" he says.

That night, they're playing the Crystal Saloon, and it's crazy, customers coming in carrying guns, the couple running the place unconscious with drink. So the guitarist and the younger fiddler end up running the bar as well as playing, while the big man gazes around with a benign smile on his face.

"Home" he says. "It's good to be home." And the guitarist serves up a Rolling Rock beer to a swaying customer, who gazes steadfastly at him before seizing him in two enormous hands and proclaiming:

"Man, you are an artist with that golden liquid, sir! An artist!"

So maybe he was, after all. An artist, that is.
Eddie Lang. Blame him.

"Electronics have ruined playing in a lot of ways. Electric guitar is kind of easy, you don't have to work at it. You just tinkle the thing and you've got the tone.

"You just have to stick at it. No matter what instrument you play, you can never be good enough. But if you say that to yourself, you might as well lay the thing doon. You can always get better, if you stick at it, practise and practise. And play with as many different people as you can, broaden your outlook, be it jazz, Scottish music, Shetland music. You've just got to learn, and that's how you learn."

THIS GUITAR SAYS GOODBYE

IT was planned as a romantic, silver wedding anniversary day out, and on the whole, things had gone reasonably well. The weather had been fine at seven, when he had stumbled blearily into the morning brightening to feed the hens and the grice, and to fetch peats for the Rayburn. He had insisted, when they put up the Fjogstad bungalow, with its triple-glazing and arctic-mocking insulation, that a solid-fuel stove was included in the ultra-modern kitchen. Jenny had fought the idea grimly, along with his desire for a range of outbuildings, incuding space for, as he had put it, "da bare minimum: twartee grice, hens and ducks." He hadn't dare mention sheep. That was too sensitive a subject.

"Whit fur do we need grice? And can we no get fine chickens at da Co-op or Presto's? Du maks plenty at da fishin, and it's me ats left here maist o da time to cope when du is aff enjoyin deeself wi di cronies in dat bliddy liner du caas a trawler. Or maist likely in port, in some pub in Ireland or Denmark. Tink o someen ither dan deesel, du bastard! And whit's wrang wi gas and electric, eh?"

Jenny had never been one to call a spade anything but a bloody shovel, ever since he'd first known her. From a crofting background herself, one of seven brothers and sisters reared in a tiny two-bedroom croft-house, her determination to rid herself of that aspect of her life, to ensure her children did not have to undergo such an upbringing, had made her implacably opposed to the reminders he liked to have around him of the past, of what he thought of as his, and the children's heritage. She scoffed when he went off in the spring to cut the peat banks which had been in the Cheyne family for generations. She never lost an opportunity to deny the value for money offered by the home-reared pork he butchered himself. But when he was at the fishing, she dealt with pigs and hens competently and carefully, as if they were part of the price to be paid for what was a genuine love, as well as a respectable, comfortable life.

"Du's juist an affal man, Victor Cheyne" she would say, sometimes at night, when they were alone - more common these days, when he was at home, since one bairn, Edna was now a pharmicist sooth, and the other, young Fergus was courting assiduously - sitting watching a movie on Sky or perhaps, if she was in a really good mood, listening to music, something light like early Neil Young, maybe, or Nick Drake. "Dy habits is aafil tryin', but if it taks a few grice and some hens, a bit o peat reek and some godless whining records ta keep dee happy....weel, du's no da ano man I cooda haed."

But that 25th anniversary morning, when he'd brought

her a Buck's Fizz breakfast, some smoked salmon, scrambled eggs, all the trimmings, she'd snarled: "Is dis dee gettin' ready to sail me aff, swimming in booze? Christ, does du want ta droon wis baith?" Maybe she was feeling the age thing. She was 48, he was 45, after all. He'd had a couple of glasses anyway, and then so did she, and her mood softened; they'd ended up staying in bed a while longer than usual, together, and the time wasn't wasted.

When they got up, the Rayburn was roaring away in fine style - completely unnecessary, he admitted, but part of the ritual he had been reared with. He placed the expensive Le Creuset kettle on the hot plate and settled down to wait until it boiled, and the unaccustomed muzziness in his head cleared.

There was no-one else in the house. Edna was in Edinburgh and Fergus had stayed over in Brae, wisely if his recent drinking habits were anything to go by. Jenny wouldn't allow the harsh words Victor felt were necessary for a 16 year old. "Does du no mind whit du was lik?" He did, though. That was the point.

Now he was remembering more, much more than he'd intended on this anniversary, allowing his mind to soar and dive along the long song that was the past, dipping and gliding like a guitar solo, full of fumbles, errors, brutal power

61

chords and the occasional perfect trill and flurry....

The weather held fair as the aluminium Voe boat rounded the Whal Horn and Da Roodrans, and the Atlantic swell hit them, mild but carrying the weighty assurance of immeasurable depths and distances. They beached at the start of the Lang Ayre, and he felt a shiver of recognition and nostalgia. Which was why they'd come. A quarter of a century before, fuelled by a case of McEwen's Export and with a cheap cassette player in the *Mary Valerie*, his father's old Shetland model, they had come here for a picnic on a perfect summer's day, and returned home with their joint future established, though Jenny's pregnancy would not be known for a month.

The ebb was almost full, so with Jenny's help he hauled the Voe Boat - he'd never named it; the thing's peculiar lack of character seemed sexless and undeserving of personality - as far as the coarse shingle would allow, then secured it with two long ropes to solid boulders above the tide line. He left Jenny unloading the food and drink they'd brought - just one tin of McEwens this time, for old time's sake, and some good South African Chardonnay, not too oaky - and went kicking along the jumble of wrack and tangle, the bruk and possible bounty of the sea, looking for firewood.

The exposed length of the Lang Ayre was rarely

visited. Accessible only by sea, it was the place where the mythical bales of cannabis or blocks of cocaine lost by smugglers might in reality be found. He had been back twice, perhaps three times since that day of glory and lust, and never seen anything resembling the package of drugs he'd once watched Customs men removing from a local lobster boat in Ullapool harbour.

At first, he thought it was just another broken piece of sea-scoured furniture, rust-stained, sand-scraped. The scrawny stalk of pale wood keeking from the red granite shingle was shaped in a somehow familiar fashion, though, and as his hand closed over the weed and barnacle-encrusted protrubrance recognition shot through him like an electric shock, catching at his breath, setting his heart palpitating. Les Harvey, he thought, that night with Stone the Crows when he touched the microphone and his guitar at the same time. A bad earth. A Bad Earth. And Alex's wee brother, Maggie Bell's lover and hero, was no more.

Victor knelt down, dropped the driftwood he was carrying and began scraping at the point where narrowness swelled into a curved, flattened shape. His fingers soon began to ache with the effort, and taking the battered Leatherman from his belt, he opened the much-honed knife blade and began working more carefully. Soon the familiar lettering appeared, faded on the worn maple, but clear nevertheless: *Fender*.

He could tell from the size of the headstock and the solid mass of rust along one edge that it was a Strat, a pre-CBS, 1962 Stratocaster. Arcane knowledge he had once flaunted so nonchalently. He pulled at the neck, still evidently a one-piece maple neck with oversized, badly corroded frets, but it was stuck fast deep in the half-sand. That meant the rest of the body was probably still there, and he realised it could only be in powder blue finish, or what was left of it, with three high output DiMarzio pickups and a replacement five-way switch, all no doubt reduced to various oxides. It wasn't guesswork. He knew. Hypnotised, he began to finger a C major chord, then a G, then a D. He began to dig with his bare, sore hands.

He remembered the first guitar he had ever seen close up, one night when Peerie Willie Johnson had been playing informally with some visiting dance band at the Ollaberry Hall, God alone knew when. He'd been a tiny peerie boy himself, and it wasn't the sound, he remembered, though he'd later grown to appreciate those flattened fifth fiddle accompaniments, those unbelievable thumb-held bass runs, the razor-sharp accuracy, timing and sheer swing of Willie's jazzy style. It was the instrument itself, the way it faced the audience. Fiddles had never appealled to him, those curled-up intimate, shy creatures, held right in at the neck or the chest, played diffidently for the sake of the player, or, with seeming unwillingness, for a dance or resting-chair hearthside audience. It was the way a guitar faced right out at the watching, listening crowd, shameless, flash, even; and loud.

Telly had brought the 1960s into their crofthouse ben-end, thanks to a hill-mounted aerial and endless lengths of army surplus co-axial cable too tough even for the hungriest ewe. Swimming, swirling images which occasionally locked clear along with the sound. And he'd seen these creatures: The Beatles, weirdly neat, uniformed, somehow dubious, slightly effeminate; the Stones, throat-catchingly mean and threatening, ugly, vicious, frightening. And with better guitars than the quaint, fragile looking things the Beatles played. And still around then, at least on the flickering pictures beamed into Ronas Voe: Bill Haley, with that huge arch-top, his lantern-jawed, fleshy face; Buddy Holly, dead, dead spotty and yet with that astonishing white, thin Stratocaster, so strangely female. That night at the hall Willie's guitar had been some old f-hole plectrum thing, he thought, rather scratchy. But it had looked so...so...what was that Glaswegian word? Gallus, that was right.

He'd gone right up to the stage at the interval, gazed up at the shining instrument, left leaning against one of those brown canvas-backed tubular steel chairs they had then, and gazed into the black cavity beyond the sound-holes, wondering what mysteries lay within.

He'd been bright; his parents had always said that, and at 12 he'd gone to school in Lerwick, to the Institute, staying in the hostel and surviving on a feral cunning he hadn't realised he possessed amid the casual brutalities and busy, crowded loneliness. But it brought music into his life in a diversity impossible north of Mavis Grind. In the late 1960s, the hostel resounded to the sound of Dansette-driven psychedelic guitar rock, the sweet, driving soul of Stax, old records from the previous generation of British jangle-pop, and the occasional Scottish country dance disc from some poor deluded foolish yokel. He met people with impressive record collections, people like Ernest Harrison from Whalsay who was an obsessive Bob Dylan fan, who introduced him over one memorable fortnight to what was then the entire canon, from the acoustic minimalism of *The Times They Are a Changin'* to the vast, odd, seductive canyons which comprised *Blonde on Blonde*. What did that mean? Blonde on Blonde? Some sort of pubic hair reference, they guessed. But then, they were just boys. Things like that were funny.

And he got a guitar.

Not much of a one, right enough. A Shaftesbury Les Paul Copy, ordered from his mam's Freeman's club book, in a kit complete with a five-watt practice amp, lead and plastic cover, not to mention Bert Weedon's *Play In A Day* instruction book. *Bobby Shaftoe's Gone to Sea*. Phew! Rock 'n' roll! That was quickly chucked aside though, because at the hostel was James, already moonlighting with dance bands at the weekend, a true six-string prodigy who could turn out a fair imitaion of Peerie Willie's ornate flurries, twang his way through any four-chord country lament you cared to mention, and yet who loved howling his way into a note-perfect Hendrix solo, given half a chance. James showed him how to do that easy three-chord little finger boogie, taught him the joys of Jimmy Reed blues, so joyously simple; things like Big Boss Man, Bright Lights Big City.

He was older, maybe 15, when James first took him to The Planets on Thursday nights. They couldn't stay late enough to hear the whole set, but it was Victor's first exposure to live rock music, high in what had once been the Rechabite Hall in Mounthooly Street, good old Jackie Sinclair, Arnie Arcus and the others. Even then he knew it was old hat, it was dance music steeped in nostlagia for what had been in the charts four, five even 10 years previously. But to feel the numbing crunch and thump deep in your chest of a bass drum, fuelled by a booming bass; to hear your ears fizz with a distorted guitar solo, through a real, battered Vox AC30; and that was surely a WEM Copycat delay on top of it.

One night he was at The Planets with Ernest, who was scathing about the "commerciality" of most of the material. But suddenly Jackie burst into *Running and Hiding*, the Jimmy Reed song, and Victor felt his guts move inside him. Ernest was shouting in his ear: "He was aye so drunk, Reed, du kens, he coudna mind any o' da wirds. His wife had to stand by him and shout them in his lug. Couldna read, couldna write. A bloody genius, man. Genius."

God, how he wanted to be up on that little stage, making these people dance, providing the soundtrack for their lives, even if it was second hand music learned off tapes, records and furious watchings of *Top of the Pops*. Later, he learned that Jackie and the boys had done just that, scribbling down lyrics for the next night's dance, to show how up to date they could be.

Six months on, another band came into his orbit: The Sons of Darkness had Che Guevara on their posters, and the name sent a pleasant chill into his heart. They played at special nights organised by the minister, priest or whatever at the English church, and they were louder, heavier, bassier; joyously frightening. Local boys, Charlie Sinclair, Andy Carter. Things were moving on. The outside world's images and sounds were in the isles. He wondered if they'd take over.

A year later, he stayed in Lerwick one weekend to hear another new group called Rainbow Pavement, and even by the sound of their name, he knew this was going to be different. It was inconceivably loud. They had Marshall stacks, wore their hair long, even in headbands, and everything about them was...big. Big Robbie Somerville on vocals had a confidence, a swagger which was hypnotic, astonishing, faintly indecent. Derek Bulter on guitar was a revelation, capable of taking well-known solos and going with them into realms which left even James slack-jawed. Women stood at the front and gawped. It hurt to see them, they were so good, although it was still other people's songs they were doing. Victor wondered at that. Surely they were good enough to produce something that was theirs, and theirs alone? But would anybody listen?

That summer, hippydom hit Lerwick big time, two years late, typically. It was 1970, and he had left the Institute with enough Highers to take him to university, which his mam and dad both wanted. He wasn't sure. The fishing had been good enough for three generations before his father, but there was something calling him away, *Something in the Air*, as Thunderclap Newman droned. And something telling him to stay. He got a job in a fish factory, just for the summer, he told himself, rented a truly grim flat in Harbour Street along with James, who in addition to serving his time as a butcher - plenty of free meat, though some of it was from distinctly odd pieces of animal - was playing three, four times a week now with a folk-rock group which churned out country, Scottish dance and even rock on occasion. He was making good money too.

And Victor had improved, could strum a reasonable rhythm pattern with nearly anything James threw at him in their late night, rum-soaked practice sessions. He learned to drink, smoke and play guitar all at the same time.

He had applied for Aberdeen University, to do history, maybe or English, and on a trip south to see round the campus blew his fish gutting savings on the Strat. He'd seen it advertised in the *P&J*, and had fallen in love with it at first sight. Bashed and scratched, yes, its powder blue finish pitted and stained with years of pub gigs. But peeping from the lush, crazy luxury of the scabbed case, it was a fantasy of stardoms past and future; others and his own; he simply could not resist it. And at £150 it was a bargain.

"Tell you, Rory Gallagher used tae own this, ma loon"

said the ravaged owner, who lived out in Bucksburn, amid countless crushed roaches and a huge Quad stereo system. "Goat tae get shot o' it, ken. Gonnie get intae management. 'S where the dosh is, ken. But ah need some up front money, ken what ah mean? Yeah, Gallagher had this in Taste. Sellt it for his 335." Which was crap. Rory Gallagher had never played a Gibson 335. The Strat was almost certainly stolen, but Victor was heading off home on the *Clair* that night, and he paid over the used tenners, left with a kind of religious, criminal joy in his heart.

Back in Lerwick, Rainbow Pavement had changed their name to Rock Crystal, and were trying new things, getting better, tougher, weirder, despite still, if pushed, being able to launch into a set of country dance tunes should the promoter of a particular event require it. Victor and James formed a band called The Transgressors, playing a mixture of electric Dylan, some rocked up Hank Williams and the usual round of chart stuff to please the punters. On drums was Keith Harrup from Burra, while the bass guitarist from James's multi-purpose money making group was drafted in with the promise of extra cash. To his own astonishment, Victor announced that he would sing.

He'd cultivated his voice in secret, a kind of rough approximation of Eric Burdon and Buddy Holly crossed with

Jagger's slurred yowl. The first time he heard it through a PA system, a terrible old Carlsbro thing, practising in the Sound Hall, he flinched in horror. But murmurings of diffident approval from the other lads made him press on. His guitar playing was competent enough, and the Strat sounded magnificently clangy through an old Fender Twin Reverb James had picked up somewhere. From the beginning The Transgressors considered themselves the cream of the local crop, the most adventurous, the coolest. "Play the Dave Clark Five" somebody shouted, at a hall hop in Vidlin. And James had coolly looked in silence into the crowd for what seemed like five minutes, before announcing "nah", and then bursting into the opening riff for *Most Likely You go Your Way and I'll Go Mine*. Ernest Harrison had been there that night, back from his sociology course at Stirling, and looking like Charles Manson. "No bad" he had grunted afterwards, and Victor had never felt so successful.

For a time, life was a wild round of drink, fags, the occasional joint, crashing out on strange floors in the back of a rancid old Transit, somehow getting to and through work which was tedious and hard but part of you, what with the banter and the tea breaks and the fact you knew everyone. And the knowledge that evenings promised music, weekends the great release of playing.

And there were women, girls, too, of course. Fumbled affairs on the same floors or in the same van he and the guys would eventually crash out in. It was the rock'n'roll lifestyle, Shetland version, small time but just brilliant when you were seventeen, eighteen, nineteen now, and university? Who needed it? This was better. Good money, filleting now on piece work, and guitars and mates, rum, red tins, roll-ups and a different girl every weekend.

Then that early summer day at home, having helped with the peats, his ma and old man sitting him down, dad pouring him a whisky and asking him what he thought he was doing with his life. Victor smiled, his best cool goofy cannabis smile - hey the straights just don't understand, du kens - and told him he was doing just fine, he and James, making quite good money, what with the filleting and all.

"Well" said his father "dat's aa weel enoff for James. He has a trade. Now, dee...." He looked nervously at his wife. "Dere's a place on dis new boat we're building, me and da boys." He took a long pull at his black rum and looked thoughtful.

"Has du no thochts of gyain tae uni, then?" His mother had seen his two older brothers off to become a lawyer and doctor respectively, and he, the youngest, had proved.. not a disappointment, exactly; boys had to have their chance to sow a few wild oats, after all. But maybe a bit of a concern. "Du kens, we'd support dee trow it. And if du still wants, du could geng. Du still hes dee highers and a."

"Na na" Victor said, sipping his own rum, feeling the warm glow and looking forward to the dance that night at the Hillswick Hall, at which The Transgressors were playing. "Dere's time yit for wirk and study. Maybe we'll tak the band sooth. James and me is writing songs, and maybe we'll tape them, mak a record." It was the first time he'd voiced his secret inner thoughts. Now that he'd said it, though, why not? His parents looked at him in silence. The radio was on in the background: Robbie Shepherd. Hardly a house in Shetland failed to have that playing of a Saturday. Bloody accordions.

That night they'd played the song James and he had written, *Run Away With Me*, a 12-bar with a melodic twist, a big jangly Buffalo Springfield chorus, and it cleared the floor in a flash. After they'd finished playing it, Victor intoned carefully that the little known Neil Young song they'd just played was going to be on their next album, and he was angrily conscious of the titters, the outright laughing. He'd forgotten how in Shetland, people who got above themselves were asking to be brought down a peg or 15. When they were packing up the gear he knocked back shots from somebody's bottle of Bells, and afterwards, at a party somewhere in

Eshaness, blacked out in the arms of some unidentified girl.

That was how he met Jenny, who quickly became an identified and constant presence in his life. It turned out he had spent the night in her arms in the back of the van, much to the annoyance of the bass player Steve, who had been forced to crash out in the cab. The other two had never bothered going to bed at all, and were still downing red tins when Jenny and Victor stumbled into the chill beauty of a glorious Northmavine morning, to find the hall, and the bar, still open. And a pony grazing on crunched up crisps up by the stage.

Two weeks later they had taken the fateful boat trip to the Lang Ayre, and when Victor found out about the pregnancy, he went with his father to see the other shareholders in the as yet unlaunched supertrawler *Fairlight*. There was a lot of murmuring, some quiet jokes, a bottle of Stewart's. When the *Fairlight* was launched in Spain, three months later, he and Jenny were there. They were living together by that time. It had seemed natural. Besides, Jenny had been keen to get out of the crammed crofthouse she shared with her enormous family. When the *Fairlight* was fitted out, he left Jenny to fly out with the other crew members, and they sailed her back, feeling like returning Vikings when they approached Ronas Voe. And the fishing began as Jenny's girth grew.

The Transgressors continued, haphazardly; Jenny said little when, after a month at sea, he spent an occasional night away playing in Unst at Saxa Vord, maybe, or down at the Sooth End. But she didn't have to. His guilt matched her unspoken disapproval. He played at home, in the house, but even that annoyed her. The Eshaness crofthouse they'd rented was too small, really, for a Twin Reverb even at low volume.

"Boys wi der toys" she muttered, heavily pregnant, flushed and breathless and not feeling diplomatic. "Is der no hoop o' dee growin' up?" He bought a little Pignose practice amp, took it to sea with him. But the dream was ebbing, the fantasy of fame retreating. The other crewmen, all older than he was, his father's age, quietly made fun of him at mealtimes. Three days after Liz was born, he was at sea, angry, hungover, frustrated at having to leave on a month long trip to Iceland for prawns, and his hands had swollen up with some kind of allergic reaction, he thought to a squid.

Almost without thinking, in a blur of depression and rage, he took the powder-blue Strat up on deck, opened the case, picked up the instrument in his sore and gnarled hands, and threw it over the side as they steamed out of Ronas Voe. He hadn't felt any better. None of the crew had said anything.

Later, in Reykjavik, he traded the amplifier for a single glass of over-proof vodka.

It was after that trip he and Jenny got married, Old John doing the business in the Heylor Post Office, baby Edna yowling in a carrycot at their side.

He had just about finished digging out the body of the guitar. It had been badly damaged by the years of exposure to sea and stone, wind and wave. So had he, but not as terminally as this. The sea had been good to him. He was now skipper of the *Fairlight III*, one of the biggest, fastest, most efficient trawlers in the entire European fleet. And he had a fine collection of music at home and on board the boat. He had kept up. He knew his Radiohead from his Verve, his Alanis Morissette from his Tori Amos. His daughter made fun of him, his son grunted at him through a face of spots, and his wife sometimes seemed utterly exasperated. But then, that was what wives were for.

The Transgressors had broken up, James and Steve the bassist rejoining the all-purpose good time band they had never really left, not....spiritually. They were still going strong, had gone almost entirely country, following demand, and recorded two or three CDs for a local label, including a special line-dancing one. They were even supposed to be doing a line dancing video which would maybe, just maybe take them to lucrative gigs south. James had never married, but the story was that he had seven children scattered about the isles, and the Child Support Agency on his back these days. So maybe he was needing to make some cash. Keith Harrup, the Burra drummer, just to spite them all, had moved south, wangled into a gig with the reformed Rubettes for a club tour, then played on a couple of crap boy band hits before becoming, of all things, an incredibly hip dance music producer. Victor felt sick every time he saw his name mentioned in *The Shetland Times*. Which it frequently was. Once he'd had to see the careers advice fellow in Lerwick about Edna, something about her daft notion to do journalism, and with a shock he'd realised that this upstanding citizen had once been a Son of Darkness, a pioneer of demonic rock music in Sheland. Things changed. People changed.

Local bands had come and gone. Tougher, younger, more sussed boys and girls, like No Sweat from Yell, writing their own material, given a hard time by the so-called Lerwick hipsters, but always good fun, the times he had dragged Jenny out to the St Magnus Bay Hotel or the Brae Boating Club. Pete Stack and da Rayburns, once a daft schoolboy punk ensemble, the inevitable two years later than the mainland - then a kind of ragged party group, before transforming themselves into an institution, a glorious soul experience every Christmas with a brass section, even, Shetland's first. They were great. They made him ache with jealousy and nostalgia. Then there were the interesting fusions between traditional fiddle, rock and dance music, like Bongshang and Rock Salt and Nails. Country bands like Sheila Henderson's terrific combo writing their own songs, doing well, sometimes playing abroad or sooth. Stalwarts, like Hom Bru, who should have been famous long ago, and now the young guns, Fiddler's Bid, all rampant testosterone and old tunes made new.

He watched and listened, bought the CDs, went to the occasional concert, made money, a lot of money, brought up his family, tried to maintain some of the traditional ways of doing things about the house, on the croft which his parents had left him and he couldn't bear giving up completely, even if he rented out some of the land to neighbours.

Did the music matter? Jenny liked to have the occasonal wild night of jigging, but she preferred the old-fashioned dances, with Eightsomes and Canadian Barn-dances and Lancers and Bostons and all the stuff he had determinedly never learned. He sat out every dance unless he was too drunk to refuse, longing for someone to take out an electric guitar, turn up a Vibrolux or a Twin Reverb to eleven and just hit the thing, send those ringing, crashing waves of distortion through his body like a storm at sea.

"Victor! Victor!" Jenny's voice was distant, wavering in the wind. How long had he been here, digging out the past? He looked at the half-excavated Stratocaster, tugged half-heartedly at the neck: it still wouldn't shift.

"Comin' Jenny" he yelled into the wind, which was really too gusty for a decent, comfortable picnic fire. Still, they'd be all right, He'd left word with the coastguard where they were, and the forecast was fine. He had his skipper's ticket, for God's sake! There was a large rock they could shelter behind, build the fire there, eat their grub. It was there a quarter of a century ago they'd....but it had been warmer then. And they'd been younger. Fitter. Passion had been more important than comfort. Maybe it still was. Maybe they needed to realise that.

He was kicking the sand and stones back into the hole he'd dug when Jenny, voice breathless and lively and full of a joy he thought she'd lost, came up behind him.

"What's dat du's fun der?" He heaped shingle around the neck of the guitar, so it could barely be seen. Some things were better left where they were, he thought. Some hopes were meant to die unfulfilled, some dreams were better untrue. Imagine being 50 and still plugging away in smokey Shetland bars, hammering out Jimmy Reed songs for a bunch of drinks, batting back requests for bloody Spice Girls singles, wishing you were Steve Earle. Thinking you *were* Steve Earle.

Christ, he thought. It would be great. It was almost heroic. Turning to his wife, he saw her smiling, teary, breeze-blown face, and the years dropped away, all 25 of them.

"Ach, never leet yon old bruk" he said. "Come lat wis git a fire gyain and open dat bottle o' wine. I'm feeling lik da years hiv juist faan aff me. Be warned. Du kens whit happened da last time we wir hereaboots."

"Du's such an aafil man, Victor" said Jenny, smiling and throwing her arms around his neck. "Does du tink du'll ever grow up?"

KIRR MIRRIN

TOOTSIE's Orchid Lounge, down on Lower Broadway, was way too good to be true. Just like the original Opry which was all restored and shining in brick, half way up the hill towards respectability. Except Tootsie's was deliberately, self-consciously...decayed. It was heritage sleaze. The walls were thick with ancient posters and yellowed photographs, everyone from Hank Williams, Senior and Junior, to Waylon, Tennessee Ernie Ford, Reeves, Cash and the inevitable Yoakam, Billy Ray Virus, Garth Brooks and Randy Travis. The floor was worn and deep in dirty sawdust puddles, the bar scuffed and scarred with a million cigarettes. It was so real it was fake. Or fake it was real. But the Americans were good at that.

Still, it had the desired effect. This, after all, really was where The Drifting Cowboys had propped up their sozzled, crippled leader prior to shows at the Opry. It was where Gentleman Jim had slipped out between sets for a quick one or 13, the smoothy devil. It was where deals were made, drugs were bought and sold, bands were joined, and drummers more often than not, sacked for annoying everyone. And now Calum was there too, sipping an ice cold Bud, stripping the label off with his fingernails, just like in that

Sheryl Crow song. Him and a bunch of skinhead teenage tourists from the midwest, who were busy sweating testosterone onto the torn vinyl of the barstools and being loud. And of course there were musicians. In a manner of speaking.

There was a tiny stage up between the door, the windows onto the street and the bar; high up, so high he thought the ancient, semi-conscious figure in the black stetson would never scale the steep steps to reach the microphone. A younger, bloated individual with a jowly, purplish face had just stopped churning out his grim Kristofferson rip-off. His own songs he'd said, frequently, desperately, panicky eyes scanning the crowd for signs of some much prayed-for record company A&R man, and finding only the desolation of tourists. When the black stetson now on the head of the geriatric wobbling up to the stage had been passed round, sweaty head-orifice dank and gawping, there had been little enthusiasm to clink any change into it.

He had rustled a five dollar note in, though. Solidarity. The guy was awful, but he was trying, and Calum was a musician too, after all. But fresh, new in town, and he knew that Tootsie's was where you came for a beer and some sentimental vibes, but only the losers ever played. Both the ones who knew they were losers and those who hadn't realised it yet.

Black Stetson Man picked up a guitar - a battered Yamaha FG-180 - which obviously belonged to the establishment. Calum was a guitar snob, and his nose wrinkled with mild disgust. He'd spent part of the previous morning in Gruhn Guitars, the most extraordinary music shop he'd ever seen, gawping and groping like some pervert in a lingerie warehouse. Martins ancient and modern. A beautiful f-hole Gibson, only $200. He had ended up buying a packet of plectrums. Plectra. They were in his pocket now, a tiny set of plastic souvenirs. Was that a song: *Plastic souvenirs were all she left me...* No. How would plectrums, plectra, ever remind a man of a woman? Of course it could be a song about guitars, a love song to frets and tuning pegs.

He had saved hard for his first Gibson J-200, and now had a small but impressive collection of acoustic and electric guitars. For Calum, playing a Yamaha you didn't own was like consorting with a possible source of infection. Metaphorically and, as he looked at this particular instrument, possibly literally.

The face beneath the black stetson was the same colour of grey as its beard, deeply etched with crevices and gullies, like bad, broken city concrete. When he opened his mouth, Calum could see no teeth. But then, this was America. No NHS here. When the sound of a lisped, toothless *Jambalaya* came buzzing from the tiny PA system, he knew it was time to leave. A bad night at the Shetland Country Club was better than this.

Then it struck him. Ever since entering Tootsie's he'd had a nagging feeling of familiarity. As he pushed his way out into the bright afternoon sunlight of Broadway, found himself staring at the original Ernest Tubb record store across the street, it suddenly clicked. It was like the Booth in Hillswick. Not the old Booth, back in the days of Big Oil, when it was knee-deep in workers from the caravan site up at the Eshaness junction, flush with cash from Sullom Voe and ready to rock and roar their way into the fathomless depths of a weekend. He'd been too young to know those crazed days, though he'd heard plenty stories about the Booth when he'd first gone there as a teenager, after the goldrush, when the construction phase was over, they were laying men off at the terminal and the pub was about to close, become the vegetarian cafe it now was. It was an echo of great, great times, the laughter of ghosts caught and held in the stones and seats and crumbling wooden walls. Lost legends.

This part of Nashville was full of that. Hatch Show Print, along the street, was another of those too-good-to-be-true preservation jobs, a printing shop open to visitors complete with original ink-flavoured dust. Still, he hadn't been able to resist buying a few of the Hank Williams final concert posters, "printed on the original type". New Year's Day, 1953 Canton Memorial Auditorium. *If the Good Lord's willin' and the creek don't rise...* But He hadn't been. And in the back of a Cadillac, the tide of bourbon and pills had risen and drowned the poor, shirvelled, nasty little genius, undiagnosed spina bifida and all. At the age of 29.

And then there was the Opry, too - the Ryman, not the Opryland theme park out of town, he couldn't stand the thought of that. He'd had to do the Ryman tour. And he'd felt it there. Felt the chill of the past. Glimpsed the tracks of the dead.

But he was here for the future. His future, his life. Not that he'd been stupid. He had an APEX return ticket to Heathrow, and he'd told everyone back home he was just going on holiday to the States. Three weeks away from the fish farm. He was owed the time, and he had the cash. He was going to tour around, have a bit of fun in Tennessee, see the sights. That's what he'd told them. He hadn't mentioned that he was taking his second-best Martin, a Herringbone D25 with him, though no doubt some of the staff at Sumburgh would have told all by now. He'd failed to mention that he was planning to take on Music City, USA, and win. It wasn't the kind of thing you dropped into casual conversation at Da Noost.

Be realistic, Calum kept telling himself. Everywhere he looked, fresh faced youngsters, younger than himself, and he considered himself youthful enough, at 29, strolled with black curved cases. At the hotel reception desk, there was a whole rack of leaflets aimed at the would-be star. Companies offering "consultancy" services, where they would, for a fee, listen to your demo and advise you on how to proceed to Music Row. They said go, they collected the $200. Recording studios, supposed managers, all kinds of people who promised that they, and they alone could help you navigate through the Nashville jungle, get you a deal, have you up there with Lee Ann Rimes in no time flat. If you handed over some cash to them first.

The hotel clerk, older than he should have been for such a job, Calum thought, had looked at him cynically.

"You a musician?" Calum had shifted uneasily on his North Eastern Farmers Dickies boots.

"Well. Yes. I suppose so."

"Got a girlfriend?"

"Well, aye...yes."

"She here?"

"Uh, no, no, she's at hame...home. This is just a sort of solo...she couldna get away...." Guiltily, he thought of Marina, how she'd looked when he'd said he was going to the States alone.

"Know what they call a musician without a girlfriend in this town, sir?"

Calum shook his head.

"Homeless. Can I see a credit card, please sir?" He'd handed his Bank of Scotland Visa over and felt vaguely belittled. But he would show them. He was good, after all. He'd proved it night after night, from the Scalloway Legion to RAF Saxa Vord, even gone with the band for a tour of country clubs in England, for God's sake, played with George Hamilton the Fourth one night in Blackpool. Well. Fourth on the bill, actually, but they'd met him, George, that is, shaken his hand. Sure it was a band, The Hired Hands, but he was the singer, and he wrote the originals they now did, 50-50 with the essential covers. He could hold an audience, could get them up dancing with the right choice of set. True, they often found themselves playing to serried ranks of automaton-like line-dancers these days, nothing but metronomic chorus-laden new country rock, like the Eagles with the middle ripped out. But sometimes, sometimes it was just magic, and it was, he was sure, his magic.

Would it work here, here where the voodoo, the white twangy spells had all been woven in the first place? He was sure it would. But his gut twisted with an excited fear at the thought of finding out.

Country music had been in his blood, his father had always said. Hillbilly tunes, they'd called them in the old days, apparently: the Carter Family, Louvin Brothers. Bluegrass fiddle, based on styles exported from Scotland and Shetland to America, now changed, charged, channeled and back across the Atlantic on record and radio, re-infecting the styles of local players with its trills and runs, its confident, swaggering swing.

Always, there had been the big singers, Reeves and Cash and Williams, and the best of the lot, George Jones and Merle Haggard. *Mama Tried* could still bring tears to his eyes. The Prison Album. God, what a gimmick. And of course it had turned out to be gimmick: *"Twenty years in prison, doing life without parole?"* Not quite. But then, in country, if it sounded real on stage or record, it was real.

Of course, he had grown up enveloped in all kinds of playing, not just country. It was like that in Shetland, and the house had always been filled with music and musicians. Shetland reels had danced, spiralled, lurched out of the hearthside at new year, and plenty other times too. His uncle and cousins had all played the fiddle, and then he'd had a flirtation with rock music, upsetting his father with punk stuff, the Pistols, the Jam, all two, maybe three years too late. That was how he'd come across Joe Ely, first of all because The Clash liked him, and that had begun to bridge the gap between him and his father. A couple of years later came Steve Earle, the *Guitar Town* album, and faider was nodding away ruefully to *The Devil's Right Hand*, and teaching him a few runs on the old Eko 12-string, set up all wrong, a very bastard to play. It had gone on from there.

His first gig, at the Country Club, the old one along from the Queens, hanging out over the sea in that tiny, jammed room, a weird cocooning cave of red velvet, like a huge hollow sofa you could climb inside. Some John Stewart songs, Joe Ely, John Prine, Lefty Frizell. Jones and *Burning Ring of Fire*, so simple, so perfect. Early George Strait, when he was good. *The Lights Are On, But No-one's Home*. Soon it was the Scalloway and Lerwick Legions, the Brae Boating Club, gradually getting together with the rest of the Hired Hands, and the beginnings of a dream. This dream.

It had been hard to hold on to it, sometimes, in the midst of continual line dancing competitions and the uncertainty of the other band members over original material. His songs. But what with Country Music Television beaming in all these smart, glamorous guys like Lyle Lovett, who was married to Julia Roberts, for heaven's sake, despite having a face like the backside of a Rayburn cooker, and that huge swathe of females, from Shania Twain to Lucinda Williams and the spooky Gillian Welch...well. They'd given it a try.

And it had taken them to...Blackpoool. Among the Illuminations, he had seen the light: hell, he wasn't going to spend the rest of his life playing *Achy Breaky Heart* to a bunch of blue-rinsed spinsters in the North of England, or Unst for that matter. He would take his music to its place of origins, to Music City, USA, and test it against the best. He had to know. Was he some third rate imitator, or in touch with anything real, anything worthwhile? Anything, to be frank, valuable. Saleable.

Now here he was. What was it The Lovin' Spoonful had sang? *There're thirteen hundred and fifty-two guitar pickers in Nashville*. And the rest. There were probably 1352 guitar players in Yell these days.

He'd done the Country Music Hall of Fame, bought about 50 souvenir books of matches; stared in awe at the RCA Studios where Elvis had recorded with the Jordanaires, and wondered if he might get the chance to nip along the freeway to Memphis, to check out Sun, Graceland. That would be a thrill. He browsed through a couple of specialist secondhand record stores; not the various Ernest Tubb branches, which were glossy and bland. He was looking for some original Carter Family stuff on vinyl, and maybe some Texas Swing for friends at home, some obscure Bob Wills. A 1950s Light Crust Doughboys LP was all he found, at an exorbitant $30. Still, you were only in Nashville once. Negativity, he thought. Stamp on it. A man could live here.

As he was leaving the record shop, he got a shock. Amid a wall of taped-up posters for forthcoming gigs, a familiar name leapt out at him. Kirr Mirrin.

He and many other stalwarts of the Shetland music scene had been stunned by the phenomenon of Kirr Mirrin, a bunch of young, traditional fiddle players who had merged a swaggering, very macho approach to traditional island reels and airs with a rock rhythm section, and found themselves swept into the world's enthusiasm for all things Celtic. It turned out being from Shetland had clout in the music world, that the likes of Aly and Tammy and Willie Hunter had created a climate where the isles were recognised for talent, and skill and original sound. And it was bloody fiddles. Of course.

What about all the people who were in love with the sound of Oklahoma and Mississippi, not the skirl of a hornpipe or a jig? Many's the pint he had sunk, jealously bemoaning the success of Kirr Mirrin, bounding about the

globe from folk festival to TV show, with two CD's out now, and, yes, he'd forgotten: doing a tour of America. It hadn't occurred to him that there would be an interest in other forms of music than country in Nashville. But that was stupid; of course there would be. He looked more closely at the poster: Kirr Mirrin were headlining at the Irish Centre, ironically enough, tonight. People around here probably though they were Irish. Well, hell mend them, he thought. He certainly wasn't coming all this way to the very holiest of country holies, to where Tammy Wynette used to live in Hank Williams' old house, where Dolly caressed her chest nightly, just to let Magnus Lindsay and his pals regale him with tales of how great they were doing on tour, the bastards. He'd been at school with Magnus. He wasn't even a real Shetlander; his parents had moved up in the very early stages of the oil developments, from somewhere like Fife, was it, or Dundee, and given birth to a child who took to Shetland culture as naturally as the average shalder. Who had benefited from the fiddle instruction that was just being made available to all schoolchildren, turned out to be brilliant, a boy wonder, blessed with feel, sensitivity and, maybe from his soothmother antecedents, a raging aggression and ambition. He wasn't afraid to let his light shine, even if it was out of his backside sometimes. Maybe that was what was wrong with himself, Calum thought, and many others in Shetland: too shy, too backward at coming forward. Too insular. Too content with the good, the magical things about Shetland. But if you live on an island, what else are you going to be but insular?

No, he had his own fish to fry. The Red Sun Cafe was waiting.

Everybody who read Country Music International knew about the Red Sun. It was where the stars, like Mary Chapin Carpenter, Lucinda, Dwight, Garth and the rest of them came to debut their own new songs, check out the opposition. It was where management spied for new artists, where people who didn't write their own stuff - all those big-haired singing waitresses - or producers searching for a hit, listened out in the hope of musical platinum dust. He'd even heard of one writer who'd had a phrase, a line, taken and used in a Brooks song, and been given quarter credit, like hundreds of thousands of dollars. That would almost do. And where the hundreds, thousands of hopefuls tried to get their names on the list of would-be performers every night, to chance their arms, try themselves in the white fire of Music City's best. Sometimes worst.

Calum knew he was not alone, that thousands had come to Nashville seeking fame and fortune, and failed. Were still failing. He'd heard that Metro police had orders to move anyone found sleeping in their cars, with or without guitar, to the outskirts of town. That every bartender and petrol pump attendant was a failed songwriter who'd handed a tape to that nice Emmylou Harris the other day, and hadn't quite heard anything back yet. Maybe next week. Next year. Never and forever amen. Hey, that was a possibly song, wasn't it?

> *Never and Forever, Amen:*
> *Will you love me?*
> *Will you think of me?*
> *Can you tell me when?*
> *You say never*
> *And forever*
> *Aaahhhhahhhhhmen....*

Hmmm. Perhaps with a little work.

The taxi ride to the Red Sun Cafe was a lot longer than he'd expected. The driver was uncommunicative.

"Songwriter?" That was all he'd said when Calum had given him the destination.

"Yeah." Trying to hide the flat, sea-girt vowels of his native isles. But he needn't have worried. There was no reply. Just a resigned nod: another hopeful loser.

When they arrived, Calum thought the driver had misunderstood him.

"No, listen" he said, "I'm looking for the Red Sun Cafe, like for musicians and....songwriters, you know, it's showcase night tonight."

The silent cab driver sighed.

"Think ah dawn't know, son?" he might have been barely five years older than Calum, if that. "Been there, got the T-shirt, now ah'm drivin' the cab. Ain't no romantic wooden shack. Through the parking lot, into the mall, past Boot World. Take mah advice, and don't expect nuthin'. Cause nuthin' is what you're gonna git, unless you're some bit luckier than me and a million others." Calum tipped him the requisite 15 per cent, and the man drove off. Maybe there was a song there, Calum pondered. Poor guy, probably he'd sold his Martin, Fender or Gibson, given up all hope of making it. *The Day I Sold My Black Guitar. Or Red Guitar.*

> *The day I sold my red guitar*
> *To make the payment on this car*
> *I settled down to write a song*
> *Had nothing there to play it on.*

As he walked through the quiet, slightly threatening mall, Calum thought of Kirr Mirrin, probably playing at this very moment to a crowd of beardie folkies, belting out old tunes, drinking, having fun, taking their own wee bits of Shetland and flogging them to the Americans. A pang of jealousy and nostalgia went through him. God, as well as Magnus, there'd be John Angus Stevenson, and that boy who'd worked with him at the cages for a while, what was he called? From North Roe, somewheres...Peter o'da Lyoag. Magnus wasn't that bad, actually. Sure, he was a bit full of himself, but, hell's teeth, he deserved to be. It was a pity he hadn't known about their gig sooner, and he could have maybe gone to the Red Sun on another night, or found some other place to showcase his talents. But no. This was it. This was his chance.

There was a crowd jostling outside the door of the Red Sun, a bizarre knot of people, all armed with guitar cases: traditional black, the blue fibreglass of 70s Martins, the worn oatmeal of old Fenders. A young woman, a dead ringer for Uma Thurman in Pulp Fiction, all black bobbed hair and bloodstain lipstick, was brandishing a clipboard and bellowing for silence.

"Now LISTEN UP! There are too many of you here tonight, as usual, and so it's a case of drawing lots for spots. Don't rush me Hon, I'm warning you." She directed this last comment to an elderly man in a black stetson. To Calum's astonishment he realised it was the same hopeless case he'd seen barely clambering onto the stage at Tootsie's earlier in the day. "We got 12 two-song spots, and I'll give you the good

or bad news just as soon as we get this thing done decently in hors d'ouevres." A bucket of plastic tokens was passed from hand to hand. Calum pulled out a 13. Good grief. *I Drew Lucky Thirteen, You Know What I Mean.*

But his number was one of those called, and he found himself inside the club, which was a cafe bar of quite astonishing blandness. Only the signed, framed pictures on the wall and the stage indicated any difference from a hundred other burger 'n beer mall joints. He'd been allowed in free, while those would-be performers who hadn't drawn a successful number, those who hadn't drifted disconsolately away, had been forced to pay a $10 cover charge, and check in their guitars at the cloakroom. Expensive disappointment, Calum thought.

Looking around, there were one or two knots of well-dressed middle-aged people who could have been record company executives, or photocopier salespeople. Who knew? Was that Kate Campbell over there in the corner, meeting and greeting? She certainly needed some new material, if her last album was anything to go by. It was hard to tell in the dim light. He perched on a stool at the bar, ordered a Miller Lite, and waited.

A large blackboard was mounted behind the stage, and Uma Thurman chalked on the running order in green chalk: number 13 was second; he was second. *I Am Not A Number, I Am A Free Man*. Too political for a country song, that. First up was a girl, California Baywatch blonde, absolutely beautiful in a blank sort of way, any age between 14 and 40, and dressed to wound in one of those Western shirts which had been tweaked in some fashionable way to look both traditional and cool. Fantastic legs. Calum's heart began to pound, and not with lust. This was worse than competition.

Uma Thurman introduced her: "An old friend of the Red Sun Cafe, newly signed to Highway Recordings and gracing us with her presence, Mizz Cora Joy!" There was warm applause, and much whoooping and hollering from the well-dressed middle aged table. Cora Joy my backside, thought Calum. Her real name was probably Fanny Sidebottom.

She was good, too, that was the worst of it. The first song was called *That's Not What Friends Are For*, and it was kind of Shania Twain out of Patsy Cline; she was competent on guitar too, playing a beautiful old Gurian by the look of it. But his listening was interrupted by Uma Thurman.

"Hi" she began, brusquely "number 13? Where you'all from?" No smile. All distracted efficiency.

"Shetland" said Calum nervously. "Lerwick. Well, really

it's Waas, but we moved...."

"You're not from around here, are yuh? Is that a Canadian accent? We get a lot of Canucks in here, you know. Jimmie Rodgers was Canadian."

"No, Shetland is...Scotland?" The woman still looked at him blankly. "England, the UK. The United Kingdom?"

"Oh! Well, yeah, good to have yuh here. You're from England! That's great! We had one guy in here the other day, a big star...what was his name, Leo Sayers? Yuh heard of him?"

Calum had thought Leo Sayer was dead, but he nodded anyway. "Scotland" he said. "I'm from Scotland. Shetland, Scotland."

"Yeah, right" she seemed abstracted. "So, two songs, then. What's your name hon?"

"Calum"

"Yeah, Calum. Two songs, don't y'all do too much, lots more to get through tonight. Good tu have yuh here, all the way from England. See yuh!" And she was heading off. On stage. Cora Joy had just finished her first song, and was introducing her next number in a melodeous Southern drawl.

"Thenk yeeew. This heeeearr's about mah ole dawg ah left behyyyyn in Mississippi...." she strummed a few chords. "Sawrrry. Got confeeeyooozed thyaar. Ah mean my boyfriend

Hank." Pause. "Easy mistake to mayyyke, girls, ain't it the truth?" Riotous laughter from what was obviously a table of close relations or people with money invested in that lovely hair. She had them in the palm of her hand. Bitch. "This is another sawng awff mah forthcaaamin' CD, Flamin' Heart. This is cawlled *Woman's Best Friend*...." God, another song with 'friend' in the title. The woman had no imagination.

Calum pushed his way to the stage while Cora took her bows, and as he opened his guitar case, and a technician handed him a jack lead, he noticed the entire table of fashionably dressed fat cats rising to congratulate Cora.... and then moving with her toward the exit. So was Kate Campbell, if that was really her, fatter than he'd imagined from pictures. Or it might have been that new age Alaskan, what was her name? Jewel. Anyway, by the time he was facing the audience, it was clear the only people left in the building were all accompanied by unopened guitar cases and a common look of sneering desperation. At least, that was all Calum could see. Uma was speaking.

"Please welcome, all the way from Scotland, England...Calum, uh, Calum... Shetland!" Christ. He hadn't told her his second name. Calum Shetland! Sweat ran into his eyes, and his teeth clattered the microphone, a spit-spattered Shure SM58, with a huge thump through the PA.

"Hi" he said. "I'm Calum Shetland." What the hell. A stage name was a stage name. Though they wouldn't like it in Bressay.

Afterwards, he unplugged his guitar, in the smattering of applause, packed it away as the man in the black stetson walked towards the stage, an ancient Guild in his hand. Calum didn't wait to hear him, just walked straight out into the muggy summer shopping mall night. Nobody took any notice. No-one came after him. No sweating A&R man ran in his wake, shouting for him to stop, that he was the next big thing, to sign on the dotted line. There were no goodbyes. Not even Garth Brooks's slave asking if his boss could rewrite one of his choruses.

He'd done OK, he thought. The two songs he'd prepared to play were ones he'd fine-honed in the Mid Brae Inn and at the Hilltop in Yell, that had convinced hard-bitten Fraserburgh fishermen in the Ferry Inn they really had been written by Ricky Skaggs, as Calum had lied. *Unhappy New Year*, with its lilting waltz time, and *She Was A Cadillac, I was a Lada*, which he hoped would translate OK. He'd forgotten to check if they had Ladas in Nashville. He'd thought of changing Lada to Chrysler, but wasn't sure if in fact Chrysler owned Cadillac. Lada it would have to be.

But as soon as he opened his mouth to sing the first

line of *Unhappy New Year*, he knew he was in the wrong place, that he was a pretender, here, a fake. He heard his voice, recognised the accent as an amalgam of Yoakam, Lovett, Williams Senior and Reeves, but could hear all too clearly the gentle rumble of Shetland dialect suppressed beneath the put-on drawl. It had sounded fine in Sumburgh. Here, it was like a terrible, cheap blasphemy. A peerie boy's karaoke showing off.

There was a little applause at the end of his first song, and he looked out on the scattering of blank, indifferent faces. Suddenly he felt horribly exposed and alone, far from home and slipping, losing his way, losing himself. Somehow he found himself fingering some unaccustomed chords, ones he hadn't played for, oh, years, and then he was saying:

"I'm from the Shetland Islands, which is sorta, halfway between Scotland and Norway...." Blankness. Nothing in response. They seemed to know nothing, nothing at all about world geography, these Americans. "Anyway, this song was written by a wife....a woman from Yell, and it's aboot da wey radiation is comin' fae Dounreay, which is nuclear...ach. Never...ne'er du mind. Dis is caad *Follow the Sea*." And he was playing Mary Ellen Odie's sweet, bitter wee song, three chords, and he could hear them talking in the audience, among themselves, ignoring him, his islands, the music, the place, the people they probably didn't even know existed. But he felt stronger than them, complete in himself. Insular. Insulated.

By the time he reached the Irish Centre, Kirr Mirrin's show was over, but there was still music coming from somewhere in the jumbled, battered complex. The cab had dropped him at the main, locked entrance, but he found a large lorry-cum camper van parked at the side, and a door nearby into the hall was half open. He went in, and the music grew louder. He knew the tune: Ronnie Cooper's *Da Tusker*. A great wave of homesickness washed over him, and he was back, a tiny peerie boy, at Hogmanay, too wee to be up really, listening in an overheated corner as one of his uncles played, waveringly, between nips of rum.

This version was faultless, though. So was the guitar accompaniment, pure Peerie Willie. His fingers itched to play a flattened fifth, to stretch away the predictable progressions of major chord country. Yet what had Willie been doing but imitating, when he heard Eddie Lang on the radio all those years ago? What was different from his own attempts to write and sing country music? Calum only knew it was. That somehow, Willie had reached out and gathered those foreign influences to himself, to Shetland, and made them new. Had never compromised his own identity. And here he was slavishly following, learning by rote, copying and not making, but faking.

Calum followed the tune through a network of dusty corridors, to a door with a computer-print out on it saying Kirr Mirrin. Without knocking, he pushed it open, and the music hit him, washed over him, sucked him in. Like the ocean. Like home.